2004 POETRY

ONCE UPON A RHYME

IMAGINATION FOR
A NEW GENERATION

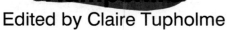

Edited by Claire Tupholme

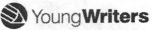 Young**Writers**

First published in Great Britain in 2004 by:
Young Writers
Remus House
Coltsfoot Drive
Peterborough
PE2 9JX
Telephone: 01733 890066
Website: www.youngwriters.co.uk

SB ISBN 1 84460 428 4

Foreword

Young Writers was established in 1991 and has been passionately devoted to the promotion of reading and writing in children and young adults ever since. The quest continues today. Young Writers remains as committed to engendering the fostering of burgeoning poetic and literary talent as ever.

This year's Young Writers competition has proven as vibrant and dynamic as ever and we are delighted to present a showcase of the best poetry from across the UK. Each poem has been carefully selected from a wealth of *Once Upon A Rhyme* entries before ultimately being published in this, our twelfth primary school poetry series.

Once again, we have been supremely impressed by the overall high quality of the entries we have received. The imagination, energy and creativity which has gone into each young writer's entry made choosing the best poems a challenging and often difficult but ultimately hugely rewarding task - the general high standard of the work submitted amply vindicating this opportunity to bring their poetry to a larger appreciative audience.

We sincerely hope you are pleased with our final selection and that you will enjoy *Once Upon A Rhyme Hampshire* for many years to come.

Contents

Hatch Warren Junior School

Laura Joyce (11)	19
Kaine Warren (10)	20
Ben Snowball (11)	20
Ollie Butler (10)	21
Sarah Dunford (10)	21
Georgie Hopkins (11)	22
Becky Reid (11)	23
Lewis Clarke (11)	24
Jessica Gyles (10)	25
Louisa Bishop (11)	26
Denisa Richtrova (10)	26
Georgina Silk (11)	27
Rosina Clarke (7)	27
Hayley Robbins (10)	28
Max Hull (8)	28
Matthew Vickers (8)	29
Rhiannon Weatherill (10)	29
Sandhya Patel (10)	30
Tristan Ford (10)	31
Danielle Every (7)	32
Alexander Phillips (8)	32
Steven Cheng (8)	33
Sean McDermott (10)	33
Rebecca Steventon (8)	34
Henry Newcombe (7)	34
Kay Wiseman-Shardlow (8)	35
Rebecca Green (8)	35
Molly Roworth (10)	36
Bradley Bostock (7)	36
Rachel Aspinall (10)	37
Emma Knill (7)	37
Katie Bennett (10)	38
Harry Liming (9)	38
Matthew Taylor (9)	39
Craig Hendry (9)	39
Grace Burt (10)	40
Savana Walsh (9)	41
Zoe Scott (10)	42
Luke Hutchins (10)	42
Hannah Byrom (10)	43
Mackenzie Collins (9)	43

Hiltingbury Junior School

Martha Day Cunio (9)	86
Sophie Kronenberg (9)	86
Lucy Andrews (8)	87
Christian Sillence (8)	87
Conor Watson (7)	87
Jason Friend (7)	88
Hannah Bosier (7)	88

Manor Junior School

Lianne Hyam (10)	88
Jasmine Stolk (11)	89
Lizzie Hogg (10)	89
Connor Burrows (11)	90
Katherine Bradshaw (10)	90
Rebecca Ellis (10)	91
Michaela Goddard (10)	91
Jasmine Burford (10)	92
Isobel Richardson (10)	93
Harrie Mort (10)	94
Tilly Besant (10)	95
Laura Randell (11)	95

Marycourt School

Jordan Roberts (10)	96
James Morgan (11)	96
Yiannis Panou (8)	97
Josephine Durham (11)	97
Charis White (8)	98
Caroline Musto (9)	98
Jack Curtis (8)	99
Alexander Morrison (8)	99
Ben Lewis (9)	100
Thomas Battersby (8)	100
Imogen Langton (8)	100
Harvey Meeds (9)	101

Mill Rythe Junior School

Jason Wakley (11)	102
Isabel Wellbelove (11)	103

Ridgemede Junior School

St Jude's CE Primary School, Portsmouth

St Peter's School, Farnborough

St Swithun Wells School, Eastleigh

Brendan Reis (9)	161
Millie Hibberd (9)	161
Ben Dare (9)	161
Kurtis Senter (8)	161
Sophia Winter (9)	162
Danielle Coombs (8)	162
Laura Moore (8)	162
Rebecca Man (8)	162
Hannah Preston (10)	163
Mark Hubbard (11)	163
Emily Lewis-Brown (11)	163
Chris Greep (10)	164

Sharps Copse Primary & Nursery School

Kelly Johnston (10)	164
Christopher King (10)	165
Jasmine Crickmay (10)	165
Liah Robbins (11)	165
Efe Gere (11)	166
Damien Wren (10)	167
Louis Landers (10)	167
Lauren Galmoye (10)	167
Kevin Draycott (11)	168
Dawn Creamer (10)	168
Karley Chandler (10)	169
Nicole Horn (10)	169

Sherborne House School

Emma Morgan (11)	170
Jenny Hadnutt (10)	170
Rebecca Thomas (11)	171
Tom Metcalf (10)	171
Matthew Crouch (10)	172
Andrew Harrington (11)	172
Joshua Peppiatt (10)	173
Thomas Bruss (11)	174
Alexa Thiel (11)	174
Jenny Patterson (10)	175
Katriina Gifford-Hull (11)	176
Benjamin Brown (10)	176

Ruby Jackson (10)	177
Stephanie Ellis (11)	178
Nikhil Bassi (10)	178
Lynn Wambua (10)	179
Lucy Higgins (10)	179
Catherine Clay (11)	180
Paulus Randall (10)	180
Kirsten Adamson (10)	181
Matthew Culmer (10)	181
Sophie Crafter (10)	182
Hollie Smith (11)	182
Adam Moussa (10)	183
Aaron Piper (10)	184
Catherine Whalley (10)	184
Sophie Bowyer (11)	185
Gemma Crouch (11)	185
Sophie Tait (9)	186
Dennis Glover (9)	186
Olivia Snow (10)	187
Oliver Dempster (10)	187
Freya Jones (10)	188
Hollie Cooper (10)	189
Charlie Clay (9)	190
Hannah Clarke (10)	190
Timothy McPhie (9)	191
Ruth Yonge (10)	191
Kay Wheatley (9)	192
Tom Caldwell (9)	192
Tristan Wong (9)	193
Anna Hannides (9)	194
Natalie Cadde (10)	194
Kari Vigor (10)	195
Anna Clark (9)	196
Henry Fenton (9)	196
Harriet Lyons-Powell (9)	197
Annabel Brown (8)	197
Oliver Hoghton (9)	198
Tom Grange (9)	199
Jack Gavin (9)	199
Millie Heslam (9)	200
Anjelica Cleaver (8)	200
Amy Cole (9)	201

The Grey House School

Whitewater CE Primary School

The Poems

Snow And Ice

Sparkling, sparkling snow,
    Cold and very white,
Freezing and quite shiny,
    Nuisance but quite magical too,
Pretty and very deep,
    Amazingly crunchy and hard,
I felt very excited!
    Beautiful and slippery too,
Oh, snow is so wonderful!

Jack Jacobs (7)
Boundary Oak School

Snow

Oh no, it is snowing!
Snow, snow, you are such a nuisance,
You delay my visits to London on the train,
But the best thing is
All the other children
Love you millions
And so do I.

Tom Stidever (8)
Boundary Oak School

Flower

F lowers are such pretty things, so
L ovely the way they look.
O ccasionally making you sneeze,
W aving in the breeze.
E ven the bees and the butterflies
R ush around brightening up the day
    as they flutter by.

Holly Lovejoy (7)
Boundary Oak School

The Earth

The Earth was born in a funny way,
First God called the lambs to come and play,
Then the bird in the sky and the lion to yawn and lie,
And then the bugs to eat and eat
And then the tiger to eat meat.
'But something is missing,' He said in a dread,
'I've got the barley and the bread.
I know, I am missing the people in the town
And that is the way the Earth is the heart of a crown.'

Kara Deering (7)
Boundary Oak School

My Best Friend

My best friend is a little brown pony,
He's got lots of friends so he's never lonely.
He whinnies quite softly when outside I go
And whenever I ride him he's never too slow.
I love him and he loves me,
So I guess that's the way we were meant to be.

Jessica Gale (7)
Boundary Oak School

Snowing

S now feels very soft,
N obody knows where it comes from.
O n the mountain it is standing,
W here its magic is always landing.
I t is very special,
N ever call it nasty names,
G randchildren are playing games.

Patrick Savill (8)
Boundary Oak School

A Caribbean Memory

Alone
On an open stretch of sand.
Only the whistle of the wind and the sway
Of tall palm trees can be heard,
Not even the squelch of a footstep can be heard.

A shell,
In the middle of the shore being washed in
And out by the waves,
A hedgehog shell all curled in a ball,
With the waves trickling through its grooves.

Crash
Go the waves against the rocks sharpening their points.
A change in weather,
The clouds go black as they blow over.

Bang!
The thunder booms like a drum,
The rain comes pouring down
As the streaks of silver lightning illuminate the dark skies.

Whistling,
The wind blows harder as it blows the clouds away,
The sun burns through the rest of the clouds
As the rays of the sun shine once again
In this tropical spot!

Dominic De Souza (11)
Braishfield Primary School

Me

I used to live in the sea,
I used to live in the sand
Until somebody found me
And took me on land.

I used to be a home,
I used to be of use
Until that hermit left me
Then I became 'aloose'.

A scuba-diver took me,
Took me back to his home,
I was lonely on that mantelpiece
And found myself alone.

I used to be sandy
With bits right in my head,
But then I was cleaned
By a very nice man called Ted.

I am completely pointy,
I am very spiked,
I am protected from predators
So they don't fancy me for a bite.

I am very small,
I think the tiniest shell in the sea.
I need to remember the washing waves,
Please could someone tell me?

Grace Dugdale (11)
Braishfield Primary School

The Jabberwock

Came with a storm,
On Monday
He made weapons of mass destruction
And army tanks.

On Tuesday
He turned all milk floats
And push bikes into cars and lorries.

On Wednesday
He turned all house into pollution factories.

On Thursday
He put all the garbage he could find
Into rivers and canals.

On Friday
He killed all animals and made dinosaurs
Come back to life.

On Saturday
He took everything from the poor
And gave to the rich.

On Sunday
He shared all his hatred with babies
So they could carry on his evil deeds.

Then he left with a tidal wave and said,
'Try and undo that goody, goody, green unicorn
With your spiral horn.'

Robert Cross (10)
Braishfield Primary School

In A Moment Of Silence . . .

In a moment of silence
I closed my eyes and heard . . .
Slaves lifting huge stones,
Druids performing magic rituals!

In a moment of silence
I closed my eyes and heard . . .
Chariots fighting with wizards,
Demons being summoned
And fire burning and crackling!
I heard gasps and shouts of Druids!

Inside my troubled mind I heard . . .
Battles with ogres,
Giants being slaughtered,
Bandits ambushing,
Dragons breathing fire and ashes burning!

In a moment of silence I heard . . .
Archaeologists gasping,
Television cameras filming,
TV presenters chatting and excavators digging.

In a moment of silence I heard . . .
The wind rustling, complete silence.

Nicholas Ballantyne (11)
Braishfield Primary School

In The Palm Of My Hand

In the palm of my hand I saw . . .
A revving motorbike zooming up my fingers.

In the palm of my hand I felt . . .
The smooth texture of shimmering, sugar-like sand.

In the palm of my hand I saw . . .
Rushing, rolling, racing waves of the huge Indian Ocean.

In the palm of my hand I felt . . .
The warmth and rays of the enormous, boiling sun.

In the palm of my hand I saw . . .
A beautiful, bright yellow daffodil sniffed by a little spring lamb.

In the palm of my hand I felt . . .
The tickle of scurrying ladybirds.

In the palm of my hand I saw and felt . . .
Everything, my hand is a crystal ball.

James Moore (10)
Braishfield Primary School

In A Moment Of Silence

In a moment of silence
I heard . . . the rustling of trees.
In a moment of silence
I heard . . . children playing next door.
In a moment of silence
I heard . . . a woodpecker pecking at a tree.
In a moment of silence
I heard . . . an owl going tu-whit tu-whoo.
In a moment of silence
I heard . . . everyone saying *happy birthday* to me,
It was excellent.

Chloe Wright (10)
Braishfield Primary School

You

You!
Your eyes are like the shimmering moon.
You!
Your lips are like red roses.
You!
Your hair sways like the grass in the wind.
You!
Your hands are as smooth as sand.
You!
Your arms are as smooth as a clay pot.
You!
Your voice is like the whistling wind.
You!
You're as strong as one thousand year-old-rock.
You!
You're as beautiful as a graceful princess.

Jonny Cooper (9)
Braishfield Primary School

In The Palm Of My Hand

In the palm of my hand
I felt tiny people running around.

In the palm of my hand
I felt hot sugary sand trickle through my fingers.

In the palm of my hand
I felt the spiky shell prickle me.

In the palm of my hand
I felt a snake slither to and fro.

Holly Thomson (9)
Braishfield Primary School

You!

You!
Your eyes are like stars in the sky.
You!
Your hair is like swaying grass.
You!
Your arms are as smooth as a stone.
You!
Your legs are like two smooth pieces of wood.
You!
Your hair smells like lemon and lime.
You!
Your ears are like green leaves.
You!
Your walk is like a pretty giraffe.
You!
Your bum is as smooth and as big a mouse.
You!
Your hands are like small palm trees.

Kelly Green (9)
Braishfield Primary School

In A Moment Of Silence

In a moment of silence I heard . . .
The mad mask mumbling mysterious myths.
In a moment of silence I heard . . .
The flapping wings of bats looking for food.
In a moment of silence I heard . . .
The chattering of chimps.
In a moment of silence I heard . . .
The sound of strong wind blowing everyone over.

Hannah Shepherd (10)
Braishfield Primary School

In A Moment Of Silence

In a moment of silence I heard . . .
The growling of cars zipping past my window.

In a moment of silence I heard . . .
The talking of people on the television.

In a moment of silence I heard . . .
The summer breeze drifting through my window.

In a moment of silence I heard . . .
The swaying of the trees settling down ready for bed.

In a moment of silence I heard . . .
People rushing past in the busy street.

In a moment of silence I heard . . .
The buzzing of the power lines.

Ashleigh Sharpe (11)
Braishfield Primary School

In A Moment Of Silence

In a moment of silence . . .
I heard the thunder of a lion.

In a moment of silence . . .
I heard the rippling waves on the sand.

In a moment of silence . . .
I heard crunching as I stepped on limpets on a rock.

In a moment of silence . . .
I heard the elegant splashes of a dolphin in the sea.

Adam Sillence (11)
Braishfield Primary School

Save Me!

Save me!
Your straggly hair smells like the salty sea water.
Save me!
Your eyes are like onions that make my eyes water.
Save me!
Your huge flappy ears stick out like fans.
Save me!
Your nose is covered in warts like an evil, ugly witch's.
Save me!
Your screeching voice sounds like a broken foghorn.
Save me!
Your neck is so short it looks as if you don't have one.
Save me!
Your arms stick out of your plump body like matchsticks.
Save me!
Your bum is so big it can't fit through the door.
                    Save me!
You're such a disgrace!

Georgia Smith (9)
Braishfield Primary School

In The Palm Of My Hand

In the palm of my hand I felt . . .
The hot sugary sand,
I saw a marble-coloured shell from the beach.

In the palm of my hand I felt . . .
The warm waves of the Caribbean Sea,
I saw the reflection of the morning sun.

In the palm of my hand I felt . . .
The whistling wind,
I felt a dancing feather touch my skin.

Hannah Jackson (9)
Braishfield Primary School

In The Palm Of My Hand

In the palm of my hand I felt . . .
Another hand clutching mine.
In the palm of my hand I felt . . .
A silver key.

In the palm of my hand I felt . . .
A sticky round lollipop.
In the palm of my hand I felt . . .
A small scrunched up blanket.

In the palm of my hand I felt . . .
A soft lock of hair.
In the palm of my hand I felt . . .
A round tennis ball.

Katrina Packham (9)
Braishfield Primary School

In My Moment Of Silence

In a moment of silence I heard . . .
The snap of a branch breaking off.

In a moment of silence I heard . . .
The whistle of the wind going to and fro.

In a moment of silence I heard . . .
The wind gently rush over the top of my head.

In a moment of silence I heard . . .
The zoom of cars whizzing past at the sound of speed.

Josh Ord (9)
Braishfield Primary School

The Jabberwocky

He came with the wind,

On Monday
He turned all army men
Into skeleton army men.

On Tuesday
He turned all schools
Into weapon factories.

On Wednesday
He turned living animals
Into dead animals.

On Thursday
He turned police stations
Into more sweet shops.

On Friday
He turned all girls
Into horrible, ugly spiders.

On Saturday
He turned good people
Into bad people.

William Pettis (10)
Braishfield Primary School

In A Moment Of Silence

In a moment of silence I heard . . .
The terrific tortoise talking to the terrifying tiger.

In the next moment of silence I heard . . .
The croaking of a bullfrog in the murky marshes.

In the next moment of silence I heard . . .
The mad mask mumbling mysterious myths.

Josie Ord (11)
Braishfield Primary School

In A Moment Of Silence

In a moment of silence I heard . . .
The hard pecks of a green woodpecker.

In a moment of silence I heard . . .
The loud buzzing of a bumblebee.

In a moment of silence I heard . . .
The gentle wind rustling through the leaves.

In a moment of silence I heard . . .
The chattering of squirrels talking to each other.

In a moment of silence I heard . . .
The squawking of birds in the tall trees.

In a moment of silence I heard . . .
The rabbits scurrying across the grass.

In a moment of silence I heard . . .
The cawing of jackdaws roosting in the chimney pots.

Sebastian Cooper (9)
Braishfield Primary School

In The Palm Of My Hand

In the palm of my hand I felt . . .
My thumb gently brush a gerbil's fur.
In the palm of my hand I saw . . .
A smooth shell show off its bright colours.
In the palm of my hand I felt . . .
Warm sea water plunge over the tips of my fingers.
In the palm of my hand I saw . . .
A chocolate bar yearning to be eaten.
In the palm of my hand I felt . . .
A pen, ready to write a fantastic masterpiece.

Matthew Harris (11)
Braishfield Primary School

Theseus And The Minotaur

Far away in times of old
Were heroes brave and very bold.
We're thinking of the land of Greece
Where many stories have been told.

Our tale today is of a man,
Picture the story if you can.
He volunteers to meet a creature,
He already has an ingenious plan.

He meets the daughter of the king
Who brings to him a ball of string.
She also smuggles him a sword
To kill the beast with a mighty fling.

He leaves the daughter all alone
With nothing but the creature's bones.
The daughter cries and cries for Theseus
But already he started sailing home.

Ellis Karsenbarg (10)
Braishfield Primary School

In The Palm Of My Hand

In the palm of my hand I saw . . . a great big castle
Where Robin Hood was saving his lady.
In the palm of my hand I saw . . . the Globe
Theatre where William Shakespeare was watching a play.
In the palm of my hand I saw . . . a pirate ship sailing
The seven seas looking for treasure.
In the palm of my hand I saw . . . a desert island with a
Man stranded on it crying for help.
In the palm of my hand I saw . . . the world.

Matthew James Mottershead (9)
Braishfield Primary School

You!

You!
Your eyes are like forget-me-nots.
You!
Your lips are luscious roses.
You!
Your fingers are dainty tulips.
You!
Your skin is like the petal of a daisy.
You!
Your hair is the clean grass swaying in the wind.
You!
You're so beautiful you make me jealous.
        You!

Christina Hodson (9)
Braishfield Primary School

In The Palm Of My Hand

In the palm of my hands I saw . . .
Osprey egg catchers doing their dirty work.

In the palm of my hands I saw . . .
Poachers in Africa hunting for elephants.

In the palm of my hands I saw . . .
Whale and shark hunters cutting down lives.

In the palm of my hands I saw . . .
Tears from families who lost relatives in the Iraq war.

In the palm of my hands I saw . . .
Love and attention to newborn babies.
That is what I like to see.

Anya Schlich-Davies (10)
Braishfield Primary School

Looking Out Of My Window

Looking out of my window I can see . . .
The city lights twinkling up at me.
Looking out of my window I can see . . .
The stars smiling down on me.
Looking out of my window I can see . . .
An angry black cloud racing over the sea.
Looking out of my window I can see . . .
The sun settling down to sleep.
Looking out of my window I can see . . .
The leaves whispering secrets to each other.
Looking out of my window I can see . . .
The moon wink.
Looking out of my window I can see . . .
Foxes and owls hunting for food.
Looking out of my window I can see . . .
The city grinding to a halt.
Looking out of my window I can see . . .
The night is awaking as day goes to sleep.

Laura Gaiger (11)
Braishfield Primary School

In A Moment Of Silence

I heard a bird in a whispering forest,
I heard a clock in the classroom go tick-tock,
I heard the wings of a butterfly fluttering,
I heard a squirrel jumping from tree to tree.

Rob Temple (10)
Braishfield Primary School

In The Palm Of My Hand

In the palm of my hand I felt . . .
The legs of a ladybird from the bush green.
In the palm of my hand I felt . . .
The gushing and splashing of the waterfall.
In the palm of my hand I felt . . .
The heart from a snake still beating.
In the palm of my hand I felt . . .
The spikiest prickle of a hedgehog.
In the palm of my hand I felt . . .
The cold from a North Pole iceberg.
In the palm of my hand I felt . . .
The blood from a cut trickling through my fingers.
        That's what I felt.

Amy Connolly (10)
Braishfield Primary School

In The Palm Of My Hand

In the palm of my hand I felt . . .
The salty sea trickle past my hand.

In the palm of my hand I felt . . .
The glittery sand slip through my fingers.

In the palm of my hand I felt . . .
The stamping and banging of the elephant feet.

In the palm of my hand I felt . . .
The dolphins splash in the water.

Pierce Fouch (10)
Braishfield Primary School

In The Palm Of My Hand

In the palm of my hand I see . . .
Waves crashing against the rocks,
Seagulls flapping their white wings.

In the palm of my hand I see . . .
Children screaming and shouting
And adults going completely mad.

In the palm of my hand I smell . . .
The salty sea going up my nose,
The engines of boats ready to go.

That's what I see in the palm of my hand.

Maisie Swayne (11)
Braishfield Primary School

Winter Is Coming

Winter is coming,
It's coming, it's coming.
The wetness and whiteness
With the sparkling diamonds
As the gold comes up at dawn!

Winter is coming,
It's coming, it's coming.
It's autumn now
With all the brightness of colours
But it will all go too soon!

Winter is coming,
It's coming, it's coming,
It's here!

Laura Joyce (11)
Hatch Warren Junior School

Bruised Brother Recipe

1 annoying brother,
2oz of cheekiness,
50oz of noise and running around,
8 pinches of blood,
1 black eye.

Mix 1 annoying brother
With 1oz of cheekiness.
Pour a bit of blood, then mix it together,
Now pour the rest of the blood in,
Put it in the oven and wait for it to start rising,
That is the base.
In a separate bowl mix the black eye
With the 50oz of noise and running around,
Now spread the icing on the base and leave to cool down.

Kaine Warren (10)
Hatch Warren Junior School

I Was Born On Friday 13th!

The open goal's right ahead,
        It's just me and the ball!
A side foot towards the goal
        But the wind carries it tall!

The coach is screaming at me,
        Now we've lost the game.
I ask God, 'Why me?'
        But it's all just the same

As yesterday and the day before,
        The day before that and now I'm hurting.
The gods are against me, are they against you?
        But this is all because I was born on Friday 13th.

Ben Snowball (11)
Hatch Warren Junior School

A Recipe For A Cool School!

1 tablespoon of theme park,
2 teaspoons of a football ground,
A wad of town centre,
1 dollop of JJs,
A dash of a cinema,
A dab of a sports room,
A sprinkle of food.

Remember!
No nerds, freaks, horrible teachers, rules!

First add a tablespoon of football ground,
Stir gently until gooey.
Next mix in a wad of town centre
And a dollop of JJs.
Then a dash of cinema,
Knead it.
After that dab on a bit of sports room,
Cook on gas mark 7,
Finally sprinkle on some food.

Ollie Butler (10)
Hatch Warren Junior School

Night-Time Poem

No stars in day,
Loads at night,
I wonder what I'll see tonight.
I wish I could be far away,
I'm dreaming that's what I might say.

I'm dreaming of a dark black sky
Filled with shining stars.
I can see far, far away,
Even Venus and Mars
When driving in my car.

Sarah Dunford (10)
Hatch Warren Junior School

Monster Stare

The door opens,
Who and what's there?
The shadows drift,
Some eyes stare.
I turn on my light,
It was only my bear!

It's night-time again,
I turn off my light.
The shadows appear,
It gives me a fright!
I get in bed,
There's only the moonlight.

I look and stare;
The door creaking,
What shall I do?
Something's speaking,
Monster stare!
Monster stare.

I'm scared! I'm scared!
Monster stare.
I'm scared! I'm scared!
Beware! Beware!
I'm scared! I'm scared!
Monster stare.

Georgie Hopkins (11)
Hatch Warren Junior School

How Come They Did That?

When Humpty sat on that wall
How was he supposed to know he'd fall?
How come the king had so many horses?
How come the king had so many men?
How come they stopped what they were doing
Just to put that egg together again?

When Mary, Mary was contrary
How come her garden wasn't scary?
How come the bells were oh so silver?
How come the maids were all in a row?
How come the cockle shells weren't described?
How *does* a garden grow?

When the cow jumped over the moon
How come the dish went off with the spoon?
How come the cat was playing the fiddle?
How come the poem's called Hey Diddle Diddle?
How come the little dog laughed at such sport?
Why can't dogs play the fiddle?

All of this happened in these short poems,
An egg on a wall, an egg who'd fall,
A cow over the moon, a dish with a spoon,
A Mary contrary, some maids in a row . . .
Weird, eh?

Becky Reid (11)
Hatch Warren Junior School

The Dragon In the Dark

From down under he sprang,
His feet lower than Hell,
Like terror he sang,
The wings mounted on his hunched shoulders,
He was ever brighter than fire.

His tail a fiery mountain,
His nostrils as dark as the darkest caves,
He roared louder than any lion,
He was stronger than hatred
And faster than a flare.

He could not be seen,
He could not be caught,
His flight was like a beat,
Standing he would have to fight.
With one eye like anger
And one like hate,
He was the most powerful creature ever to be made.

He belongs in Hell
And tramples the ground to dust
And cities to ruins.
A dragon he is and a dragon he'll stay,
A guardian of the underground passages to Hell.

Lewis Clarke (11)
Hatch Warren Junior School

The Staffroom!

People are dared to go in,
Some say they hear screams
Or is that in their head?
I would love to go in there
But is it dangerous?
Oh no, it's my dare
To go in there.
I am breathing in and out,
I step closer to the door.
My hand shaking,
Then the door flew open.
It was my teacher Miss B.
She asked what I was doing.
I was just looking in the room,
It was painted in light colours
With cakes, cookies, chairs,
Sofas and a plasma.
Then I heard a scream,
It was the TV!
I know I should keep it a secret,
And keep the rumours going?
It's my secret,
I'll keep it.
No one will know, just me.

Jessica Gyles (10)
Hatch Warren Junior School

Partying Sheep Galore

I never felt suspicious about sheep
Until one day I heard them speak.
I turned to look at the herd of wool,
I saw them dancing, that looked cool.
Once again they started to say,
How is your glorious day?
When I looked again my sheep had changed
In to a groovy blue DJ.
The sheep all started to bop and rock,
The rest of them started to slide and glide.
An hour or two had passed,
Of manic sheep galore,
The party started to die,
At this I do not lie,
For the partying sheep had gone.

Louisa Bishop (11)
Hatch Warren Junior School

Goldie

Goldie was sitting one day
And thought of an idea
Which came straight away!
I will go for a walk
And on the way I'll talk away.
She saw some food
And hurried to get it,
But somehow missed it.
Nobody saw her afterwards,
I think she starved to death!
And this is poem of Goldie Locks.

Denisa Richtrova (10)
Hatch Warren Junior School

The Day The School Flew Away!

I thought it would be a fine day,
But when I woke up I saw a spaceship fly away,
I didn't think that I'd see it again until it was break.

It was flying a long way away,
Then we went into class, did some maths,
But then I noticed something strange,
Argh! My teacher had turned green!
I ran to the headmaster,
But when I turned the handle
It turned to slime.

I heard a rumble and sparks went off,
I got outside just in time,
Before the school flew far, far away!

Georgina Silk (11)
Hatch Warren Junior School

Valentines

V alentine is when you give things to people you love.
A card is great but presents are better.
L ovely presents, open them up, see what you get.
E veryone might go out for dinner with your families.
N uts and pasta that's what you want or do you want
   everlasting gob-stoppers?
T ea, coffee, what do you want?
I love Valentine's Day so much.
N ow it's the end of the day,
E veryone gets into their warm beds.
S leep tight, hope the buggies don't bite!

Rosina Clarke (7)
Hatch Warren Junior School

Winter

Winter is cold,
It's extremely bold.
Children wrapping up warm
To keep away from the storm.

Winter is dark
Even in the park.
The day disappears,
Then the moon reappears.

Everyone stays inside,
The wind blowing wide.
Someone is sneezing,
The baby's wheezing.

Legs prickling in the breeze,
Everyone eating bread and cheese.
Blankets needed as the night comes
And cuddles from our mums.

Hayley Robbins (10)
Hatch Warren Junior School

In The Giant's Pocket

In the giant's pocket I found . . .
One flat football,
Two dead ducks,
Three fat frogs,
Four smelly socks,
Five mouldy melons,
Six sweaty sausages,
Seven silver sandals,
Eight big buses,
Nine fragile flowers
And ten poor poodles.

Max Hull (8)
Hatch Warren Junior School

Thank You Mr Carter

Thank you Mr Carter
For coming to our school,
We really liked your poems,
They were very enjoyable.

Thank you Mr Carter
For coming to our school,
You played your guitar very well,
Right at the back of the hall.

Thank you Mr Carter
For coming to our school,
I hope you enjoyed it
Because you really rule.

Thank you Mr Carter
For coming to our school,
Your guitar is very big
But brilliantly cool.

Matthew Vickers (8)
Hatch Warren Junior School

School Poem

I went to school today,
I saw lots of teachers on their way,
It's time to say 'Good morning,
How are you?'
Time for class now, it's literacy,
Oh no!

Lunchtime comes, time to eat,
After school, I go back home,
To a lovely bed,
I'm cold and very alone.

Rhiannon Weatherill (10)
Hatch Warren Junior School

Monster In A House!

There once was a hairy creature
Who stood from me about a metre.
He was very green
And certainly unclean,
I bet you he was a marvellous eater!

So then one day
I went away
To find a clear white bottle,
So hopefully the monster would have a very nasty topple.
After that the monster should go away and possibly decay.

I suddenly went to the bath
For I knew the monster wasn't far.
I had the bottle just for safety,
For I knew the monster was very crafty.
I also turned the lights off just for a laugh.

And uh oh! The monster's come!
Probably just for some creepy fun.
So I hit the bottle on the monster
Which ran around like a rooster,
Then disappeared at the rising sun.

After all that spooky fighting,
It's time I got some proper sighting
Of cool sweet dreams.
Hopefully not full of monster gleams,
Which will switch off my hall light's lighting.

So there you go, the monster's dead,
Glad it wasn't me instead.
Stupid, how there's a monster in the house
Which always stays silent like a mouse.
Oh well, see ya! I'm off to bed.

Sandhya Patel (10)
Hatch Warren Junior School

Celebrations

My mum bought some Celebrations,
It's my favourite sweet.
She said not to eat them until Christmas Day
But I couldn't wait until then.
I creep downstairs,
I saw the tin of Celebrations,
I'll just eat one,
So I ate one
And another and another.
Then I suddenly noticed
They had all gone!
I thought of a good idea,
I crept into the kitchen
I got some tin foil,
I went back to the sweet wrappers,
I filled them with tin foil sweets,
Perhaps they wouldn't notice.
I put the lid back on the tin
And went back to bed,
I was full of gorgeous sweets.
Next morning
I went downstairs for breakfast,
We all sat in the lounge
Opening Christmas presents,
'Who would like some Celebrations?'
I was suddenly nervous,
They all took one,
The wrappers were opened.
'Tristan.'
They knew it was me.

Tristan Ford (10)
Hatch Warren Junior School

Thank You Mr Carter

Thank you Mr Carter
For coming to our school,
For sharing your poems
With us all.

Thank you Mr Carter
For coming to our school,
You're good on the guitar,
It is punky and cool.

Thank you Mr Carter
For coming to our school.
I hope that sometime
You will come and call.

Thank you Mr Carter
For coming to school.
I liked it when you did electric guitar,
It was very enjoyable.

Danielle Every (7)
Hatch Warren Junior School

The Brilliant Sun

The sun glistens on the sea,
It sends down rays of light to Earth,
The sun shines down on me like a giant spotlight,
It shines upon the sand to make it glow,
The sun is so hot if you touch it you will lose a finger,
It is hotter than fire,
Without the sun we would live in darkness,
There are a lot of flames in the sun.

Alexander Phillips (8)
Hatch Warren Junior School

Thank You Mr Carter

Thank you Mr Carter
For coming to our school.
Your poems are really great
And really, really cool.

Thank you Mr Carter
For coming to our school.
It's a good thing you didn't have a poetry duel
Because you would really rule.

Thank you Mr Carter
For coming to our school.
You and your guitar are brilliant
And very enjoyable.

Steven Cheng (8)
Hatch Warren Junior School

Parents' Evening

Parents' evening is the most scary thing ever,
It seems Mum's in there forever and ever.
Once in a while
They lose their smile.
When they come out
They scream and shout,
'You've been bad
And made me sad.
Wait until I tell your dad,
You know what he will say,
You're grounded from today.'
I hate parents' evening,
Can't wait to get home!

Sean McDermott (10)
Hatch Warren Junior School

Thank You Mr Carter

Thank you Mr Carter
For coming to our school.
Your poems are really good
And so are you all.

Thank you Mr Carter
For coming to our school.
Your guitar is brilliant
And it's very, very cool.

Thank you Mr Carter
For coming to our school.
I really enjoy your poems,
I really enjoyed them all.

Thank you Mr Carter
For coming to our school.
You are really brilliant
And your poems are very cool.

Rebecca Steventon (8)
Hatch Warren Junior School

Thank You Mr Carter

Thank you Mr Carter
For coming to our school.
I like your poems, they are the best,
So please come again.

Thank you Mr Carter
For coming to our school.
It was neat meeting you.
You are the best poem writer in the world, I think.

Henry Newcombe (7)
Hatch Warren Junior School

From The Bottom Of My Garden

From the bottom of my garden
I found a pretty rose,
I picked it up and pricked myself
And drops of blood fell down.

From the bottom of my garden
Under the pretty rose,
I saw a family of worms
Wriggling on each other.

From the bottom of my garden
I found a pretty stone,
Under the pretty stone was a woodlouse,
A woodlouse as grey as can be.

From the bottom of my garden
I found a sparkling thing,
I didn't know what it was
But when I got closer
It was my ring!

Kay Wiseman-Shardlow (8)
Hatch Warren Junior School

The Golden Sun

The sun shimmers in the darkness,
It glistens on me,
The sun is as hot as ash,
It glows on the glittering sea,
The sun flickers in the sky like fireworks,
It burns me when I'm out,
The sun sparkles on the ground,
It makes me brown when I'm lazing about,
The sun is really bright,
It shines on my bed at night.

Rebecca Green (8)
Hatch Warren Junior School

Carried Away

Do not put down
A good book to read,
For all the places it could lead.

I'll be lost in a world of fantasy,
Monsters and dragons chasing me
And my thoughts will be far away.

Princesses, princes,
Witches and wizards,
A magical, dreamy land.

I'll read and read,
I'll never stop
Until I reach the end.

Oh, how I wish I could read
Each day from dawn to dusk,
But then I'd get . . .
                        too carried away!

Molly Roworth (10)
Hatch Warren Junior School

The Colours Of The Rainbow

Red is the colour of a rose,
Blue is the colour of the sea,
Yellow is the colour of the bright sun,
Green is the colour of grass,
White is the colour of clouds,
Brown is the colour of a box,
Black is the colour of a dark, dark night.

Bradley Bostock (7)
Hatch Warren Junior School

Spying On My Teacher

Shh!
I'm spying on my teacher,
Just for this weekend,
No one knows.

She goes into her Mini,
Oh, this is good!
She's at her house,
It's the street next to mine. Oh no!
There's a man in there!

Shh!
I'm spying on my teacher
Just for this weekend.
Let's get on with it,
This is the good bit.

The man's taking her to dinner,
The best restaurant in town.
Yuck, here comes the disgusting bit,
Shut the camera down!

Rachel Aspinall (10)
Hatch Warren Junior School

Red

Red is the colour of roses,
Blue is the colour of posies.
Purple is the colour of an aster,
Yellow is the colour of pasta.
Brown is the colour of trees,
Black is the colour of bees.

Emma Knill (7)
Hatch Warren Junior School

My Fish

I bought some fish the other day
And overnight they ran away
Or so my dad said.
They hopped and skipped along the ground
And under the gate without a sound
Or so my dad said.

They were on the drive and round came a car,
They jumped and bounced onto the path
But they were too late
Or so my dad said.
But they were too late,
The car wheel ran over the fish,
They were dead!
Or so my dad said!

Katie Bennett (10)
Hatch Warren Junior School

Dinner

Dinner time is very nice,
We all like to eat
Pizza, chicken nuggets and chips.
Pudding is after dinner, yum!
We eat our food to make us grow.

Babies mess around with their food
But we eat properly with our knives and forks.
We have ketchup on our dinner,
I love dinner time,
It's nice to eat as well.

Harry Liming (9)
Hatch Warren Junior School

Pirates

Cool people are pirates,
Nothing is as good as them,
They are so mean
But, they can still die.

They go with mean sails,
Argh! Skull and crossbones
And a spooky ship.
What I hate is hats.
I really love *cannons, cannons!*
And also love the *cannonballs!*
The chief pirates are very, very mean,
Pirates don't go to school.

They are as smashing as a sumo wrestler,
They are like lords,
Cool people are pirates,
Nothing is as good as them.

Matthew Taylor (9)
Hatch Warren Junior School

Henry VIII

As you all know King Henry VIII had 6 wives
Including Anne Boleyn.
He kept an album with all their photos in.

As Anne Boleyn was sat on her knees
Dressed in her very best frock,
King Henry shouted, 'Smile please love,'
As her head rolled off the block.

She lost her head
But she kept her smile.

Craig Hendry (9)
Hatch Warren Junior School

Questions

'Mum, could I have a dog?
Mum my friend's dog's just had puppies,
Mum, if I had a dog it would give me exercise,
If only I had a dog!
Mum, please, please, please!
Mum, all my friends have got a dog,
Mum, it's not fair!
If only I had a dog!'
'But if we went on holiday.'
'Nan could look after it.
You had a dog when you were younger!
So why not me?
If only I had a dog!
Fine, then a cat,
But dogs are better,
Besides they do a lot more!
If only I had a dog!
Mum, of course I'd want a girl,
Mum, we'd need to breed it!
Then we'd get more puppies for us!
If only I had a dog!
Maybe the neighbours could look after it instead,
I'll train her to do her business outside,
And you . . .'
'No!'

Grace Burt (10)
Hatch Warren Junior School

In The City

In the city, dark at night,
Fireflies,
Such a sight.
Neon lights
Shine so bright.
No one's cars starting motor
Dare upset the peace
In the city,
Dark at night.

In the city, dark at night,
No aeroplane takes flight.
No screaming child,
Or howling wolf
Dare upset the peace
In the city,
Dark at night.

In the city, dark at night,
Lights from the cinema
Shining quite bright.
Enjoy the moonlit sky
Because in the day
It's the sunshine's ray.

Savana Walsh (9)
Hatch Warren Junior School

Parents' Evening

Do you know
When your teachers say,
'Time for letters,'
And she looks at you
And smiles an evil smile,
What could it be?
Swimming?
No, we did it last week.
What could it be?
Oh no, not parents' evening.
Run, hide, leave the city,
Leave the planet.
So on Monday the 5th
I go to parents' evening,
I sit and cry,
I feel like I am going to die.
The shadows move, they come out,
I'm off the hook, I'm free, I'm free,
And then she says,
'Until next time . . .'

Zoe Scott (10)
Hatch Warren Junior School

Ice Cream

I like ice cream very much,
It's cold and icy to the touch.
Lots of flavours you will love
But my favourite is chocolate.
Ice cream melts upon my tongue
And it tastes yummy.

Luke Hutchins (10)
Hatch Warren Junior School

Literacy

'Everyone get your literacy books out.'
This is so boring.
'Four page story please for our display.'
Pardon me, did my hearing go funny?
I couldn't even do half a page because I can't start a story,
She must know me by now.
'You've got just half an hour left.'
Bum! I've only written one sentence and that's copied from the board,
I shouldn't have said that,
The teacher's heard she's walking very quietly and slowly,
I can wait to get told off, it's just not fair.
'Time's up.'
Pants!
I'm going to get detention
Like every time.
'Work in please Fred.'
'Um . . . um . . . um.'
Here comes the teacher again,
Oh no
Too late!

Hannah Byrom (10)
Hatch Warren Junior School

Burger!

B elly rumbling, belly crumbling,
U rging to eat it, urging to beat it,
R umble, rumble,
G reat burger lads,
E ver more I can say,
R umble, rumble I'm so full,
    Rumble, rumble time for school.

Mackenzie Collins (9)
Hatch Warren Junior School

Through The Door

Through the door there is a place
Where we can sit in grace,
Don't be afraid we can sit here all day
And have a good play.

Through the door there is a leopard
With paws to soften the step,
Look here comes a shepherd,
Oh no! He's been ate.

Through the door there is a river
Where fish swim free.
I think I'm about to quiver
There's a monkey up that tree.

Richard Pougher (9)
Hatch Warren Junior School

Diggers

Enormous digger,
Tiny digger,
Engines roaring,
Yellow JCB,
Mud covered,
Never clean - always dirty.

Gigantic arms with buckets scooping,
Moving, grabbing, pulling lifting,
Monster wheels and monster tyres.

Flicking the mud up as they move about,
Getting the job done.

Tim Bevis (10)
Hatch Warren Junior School

My Big Sister

My big sister,
With long blonde hair,
Big and mean
And never fair.

She talks a lot,
She never stops
And worst of all
She's lost the plot.

She's absolutely mad,
She's crazy,
She throws away
My chains of daisy.

My sister has the name of Gabby,
She could be there or here,
Keep your eyes peeled open for her,
When you see her do not fear.

Danniella Tyler (9)
Hatch Warren Junior School

The Sounds Of The Night!

The mist rises
As the night drew in,
Temperatures, drop,
Trees creak,
The eerie sound of a mouse squeaks,
The river runs faster,
Now splashing, jumping around meanders.
The moon peeks out of its clouds,
The woods look darker now,
Rabbits run into holes!
The wind starts to blow,
Running stops,
The dusk is here!

Laurence Cristofoli (10)
Hatch Warren Junior School

My Friend Paul

At school, my friend Paul,
Oh no, where is he?
He's at the office,
Why? He's being sick,
What are we going to do?
Then Mrs Martin came in,
'I got a note about Paul,
He's gone home.'
'But we need him for our group.'
'You can have John,' said our teacher.
'Ohhh!'
'Don't be mean you two.'
'But I've found a group Miss.'
'OK, you two pick a group, but not together.'
'I'm with Jordan, Pete and Bob.'
'I'm with Harry, Mike and Josh.'
'Ha-ha.'
'Don't laugh at me.'
'Come on you two, it is nearly end of school.'
'But I want to go home.'
'Only 30 minutes left.'
'But it was home time ages ago for my friend Paul.'

Elizabeth Eggleton (9)
Hatch Warren Junior School

Fantastic Football

A shot comes in,
Oh he's hit it wide.
Goalkeeper kicks it,
Up the field it goes.
A header flicked on,
Here's a shot.
No, he's hit the post,
It's come back.
A volley,
No over the bar.
Half-time's come,
The second half's started,
They're passing the ball well.
A shot.
A good save by the keeper,
Now a corner,
It's come in,
A header,
It's a goal!
Half-way through the second half,
The other team playing rubbish,
But here's a shot,
They equalised.
The whistle's gone,
It's a draw.
Next match,
Tottenham Vs Portsmouth!

Charlie Knapp (10)
Hatch Warren Junior School

Dogs

Dogs, dogs,
Strange little dogs,
They're funny things,
Always running about,
Barking a lot,
Panting as well,
Chewing things
They shouldn't chew,
Digging up bones and stuff,
The stuff they dig up
Isn't for them,
It's for you,
You give them treats
For being good
But when they're bad
Argh!

Charlie Mitchell (10)
Hatch Warren Junior School

Venice

Venice, Venice
The city of water,
It glistens, sparkles too.
The shimmering fish glide through the water,
Long, pointy sails soar through the air.
The harbours glitter
In the sun as it sets
To the ground,
And in the evening
It never stops
But the water carries on singing.

Sophia Rapacioli (9)
Hatch Warren Junior School

War

Boom! Boom!
Have a broom,
Clean the trench,
Don't sit on the bench.

Boom! Boom!
Use a spoon,
It's World War I,
You cannot run.

Boom! Boom!
Over the top,
Grenades go pop.

Boom! Boom!
Guns stop.
Wa hey, we won the war!
Boom! Boom! Racer, racer boom! Boom!

Robert Butler (9)
Hatch Warren Junior School

Me

T en years old, Tyler is his name,
Y apping on about having some fame.
L oves to play footy every day,
E very time he scores, *hooray!*
R eading is his big dislike.

A lways riding on his bike,
N utty sometimes at his school,
D ives into the swimming pool.
R acing it's always the same,
E ven being very lame.
W inning every footy match,
S houting, 'Get the ball in catch!
    Yeah!'

Tyler Andrews (10)
Hatch Warren Junior School

Need For Speed

My name's Josh,
I have lots of dosh.
I'm very, very posh,
Oh my gosh.
Look at the time,
We have to move on.
Here's the story about me
Buying a Mitsubishi Eclipse,
Customising it into a top model,
Pro engines and exhaust,
Pro brakes,
Pro drive drain,
Pro ERU fuel systems,
Pro tyres,
Pro turbo packages,
Pro nitro systems,
Full acceleration,
Full top speed,
Full handling,
Cars style 10 stars.
Racing down the street at midnight,
Thrashing the gang with my nitro boost,
Coming first place, yeah.

Joshua Rappolt (9)
Hatch Warren Junior School

Winter

I opened the door one morning,
The cold hit my nose in two seconds flat,
I looked out at the mountains
And the river flowing down,
Ducks hiding under over-hanging branches.

Matt Hagan (9)
Hatch Warren Junior School

Freedom And Crowded

I wouldn't like to be in school,
I'd be somewhere free on the seaside
And look out onto the horizon's view,
Watch the sun go down
And watch darkness come and be alone.

I'd get on top of a mountain
Looking out everywhere in my view.
I'd rather be in a football stadium playing for Chelsea.
How could I get all that rather than be in school every day?
How would it feel to be in Italy, Spain, Mexico, France,
Germany, Holland and America?
I'll play football in one of those countries,
I'd be free,
I'd play any old sport.
I'd be in Australia,
I'd be in Greenland.

Nicholas Barlow (10)
Hatch Warren Junior School

The Mystery Monster

It sneaks upon you at night,
Creeping and crawling.
Lives in mountains
And lakes.
Hiding
From the human eye.
Walking in the shadows.
No one can see it,
Not me or you.
He's nowhere to be seen.
He's as slimy as a snake
And as sly as a fox.
You never know where he is.
Over here, over there,
He's a mystery monster.

Lauren Palmer (9)
Hatch Warren Junior School

I Hate School

I hate school,
It's soooo boring,
Teachers telling you what to do.
'Get a pen!
Not a pencil!
Put that in your tray!
You should have handed that in!
Be quiet,
Stand in the corner!
Your name's on the board!
You've got a detention!'
But the bit I love most
Is break,
Where you can shout
And play
And tell your friends
How silly the teachers are,
Then when you come in
The teacher's there
Just staring at you,
Then they go red
And scrunch their hand into a ball,
Then blurt out
And shout,
Then yes
It's nearly home time.

Jenna Rose Silk (10)
Hatch Warren Junior School

A Very Crazy Animal Alphabet

A bsent aardvarks
B ossy bears,
C ocky cats,
D umb dogs,
E ccentric elephants,
F unny frogs,
G oofy goats,
H ippy horses,
I gnorant iguanas,
J igsaw jaguars,
K icking kestrels,
L oopy lions,
M ad monkeys,
N asty newts,
O bservant octopus,
P oppy appeal python,
Q uestioning quails,
R atty rats,
S tupid stick insects,
T ip top tigers,
U nder the weather unicorns,
V ictorious vultures,
W icked whales,
X -ray foxes,
Y oung yaks,
Z ippy zebras.

Harry Stone (11)
Hatch Warren Junior School

I Hate School!

I hate school
And a class rule!
It is, we have to co-operate
Because I only have one mate.

I hate PE
Because we have to do rugby!
We go on the computer and type with a keyboard
And if I get angry I would like to stab the teacher with a sword.

When we do art,
I never take part
And when I do football I kick the ball,
Then in my worst dreams we have to go back to school.

I can't wait to go home
And play with my mini Millennium Dome.
Oh! And play pool,
This is a fact, *I hate school!*

Martin Hill (10)
Hatch Warren Junior School

The Dragon

Beyond the dark, snowy mountains a fierce dragon lives,
It lives in a dark, forbidden cave.
You can hear its teeth smashing together.
You can hear echoes of its feet cracking bones where explorers
Came to explore but they failed.
Flames burst out of the cave door
As it roars.
You can hear the dragon's cry of anger,
But then a huge *burp* appears.
The dragon stops crying and starts roaring,
'The dragon is cured,'
Say the people who live near the cave
And the mystery is solved.

Ben Childs (10)
Hatch Warren Junior School

A Recipe For A Sad Teacher

4 teaspoons of tears,
1 cup of noise,
20 tablespoons of chattering,
1 pint of dumb brains,
5 dollops of no homework in.
Now I have all my ingredients
I just need to add it together like this!
First, put the cup of noise in a bowl,
Then add in 4 teaspoons of tears
And stir till like cream.
Next sprinkle in 20 tablespoons of
Chattering in a bigger bowl,
With the 5 dollops of no homework in
Beat it till water-like.
Now you can add 1 pint of dumb brains in the big bowl.
Mix both mixtures together.
Put in oven at gas mark 4.
Wait for 10 minutes and then leave to cool down.

Jone Jone Chun Leung (9)
Hatch Warren Junior School

A Recipe For A Baby Sister

2 pints of nappy wetting,
1 teaspoon of baby powder,
I pinch of cheekiness,
A dash of a baby girl with anger,
As well as a whole 3 pints of tears
And a chunk of rosy cheeks.
Mix well until smooth,
Pour into a tray with snoring foil,
Cook for baby sleep time,
Sprinkle anger from the tired parents,
Then leave to sleep until they cool down!

Daisy Wilson (10)
Hatch Warren Junior School

A Sad Headmaster

For a sad headmaster you will need:
10 teaspoons of tears,
1 big headmaster,
1 enormous bowl and spoon,
4oz of water,
1 sad face and
10 butterflies.

First you take your headmaster,
Then you take your enormous bowl and your large spoon,
Next you take the 10 teaspoons of tears.

Now you mix the headmaster and the 10 teaspoons of tears
In the enormous bowl,
Then mix until the headmaster is crying.
Then you tear open the headmaster's tummy
And put the live butterflies in.

Next you add the sad face and the 4oz of water
And there you have your sad headmaster.

Chloe Bond (9)
Hatch Warren Junior School

America!

A merica is the land of fun,
M agic Kingdom has the attractions for peaceful calming,
E veryone is kind and caring.
R ides are cool but also scary,
I slands of adventure is the place for roller coasters,
C areful not to go on rides that could be way too scary,
A merica it's cool, go now!

Donna Howick (9)
Hatch Warren Junior School

Super Striker

I am the striker from Lonsdale farm,
When I get the ball I am very calm.
I don't hog, I don't do anything flash,
I just get the ball and get the cash.

I wish I could be a goalie
Saving all those shots,
Then go down the pub
And have a few vodka shots.

I wouldn't mind being a midfielder
Passing the ball around,
But then meeting a drunk person
And getting a pound.

I would hate to be a defender
Tackling all the team,
But the thing that puts a smile on my face
Is going home and having a dream.

Ryan Mcguire (9)
Hatch Warren Junior School

Lessons

L iteracy causing chaos,
E xpensive elephants for the school pets,
S illy school children selling sausages at breaks,
S assy rats selling stupid steaks,
O ranges being given away,
N aughty children saying, 'No way.'
S uitable school geeks saying, 'OK.'

Katie Troddyn (10)
Hatch Warren Junior School

My Baby Brother

My baby brother
        screams and shouts,
He eats his veg but not
        his sprouts!

When my friends come
        round to play
My baby brother runs away!

He loves to come
        up in my room,
He loves to make
        me full of gloom.

My baby brother screams and shouts,
        he eats his veg
        but not his
        sprouts!

Jordan Mahoney (9)
Hatch Warren Junior School

A Sad Mum's Recipe

What you need -
Bowl, a crying cup
And a spoon.
Put a teaspoon of sadness in a bowl,
Then a chunk of badness in a mini bowl,
Then put in a sad face,
Pour in a detention letter,
Drop in a snapped piece of grumpiness
And lumps of non-eaten sandwiches,
Pour in a snapped school pencil
And a ripped school book
And there you have a sad mum.

Lewis Maton (9)
Hatch Warren Junior School

Fiver On The Floor!

When I went to school on Monday
I saw a fiver on the floor,
I had no idea what to do!
But then it came to me like a bolt of lightning,
I could keep it and buy ten videos
Fifty pence each from Asda,
But would I ever watch them?
Or maybe I should give it to the police,
They might give £1,000 in cash!
Or give it to my mum,
She'll be well pleased.
Could I share it with my friend Lisa?
We're going shopping on Saturday.
So it's between me, police, my mum or Lisa.
I actually left it there,
But when I was at the gates
I found twenty pounds!
What a nightmare.

Lauren Strange (9)
Hatch Warren Junior School

Crazy About Sport

B isons rule!
I nvictors suck!
S kate hard,
O ffside,
N o penalties,
S core!

L eeds rule!
E verton suck!
E veryone shouts.
D anny Mills
S hoots and scores!

Dominic Duff-Cooper (10)
Hatch Warren Junior School

My Baby Sister's Recipe

First get a bowl,
Then get 5 teaspoons of baby liquid,
Put in bowl,
Add 2 ounces of milk,
Stir fast,
Get 3 teaspoons of chicken and rice,
With sweet and sour rose cheek sauce,
Then add 45 pounds of terrified tears,
Whisk thoroughly, then put in oven for 5 minutes.
Take it out of oven with oven gloves.
Add 2 pounds of babygros,
3 pounds of tears
5 pounds of nappies,
Bake in over for 2hrs 5mins,
Take out, leave to cool.

Kira Barnes (10)
Hatch Warren Junior School

Golden Dragon

G olden dragon,
O ver me,
L icking nectar,
E ating humans,
N ext day comes.

D ragon,
R uby eyes,
A beautiful sight,
G o swift gold blur,
O n wings of golden steel,
N ext dragon comes,
　　　　Pause and listen
　　　　For the whisper of wings.

Denise Edmed (10)
Hatch Warren Junior School

Jim Da Pin

There once was a pin called Jim,
He lived in a castle
Which really was a parcel.
He went outside
And started to fly
On a paper aeroplane.
It started to rain.
He crashed to the floor
Not 'appy any more!
He said,
His face is going red,
I wanna get back to me castle
Which really is a parcel.
He went to a boy's house
Lookin' for a toy house
He jumped in his monster truck
Skiddin' in the sloppy muck,
Thank God I'm home
No winds like cyclones.

James Smith (10)
Hatch Warren Junior School

Chelsea Rule

C helsea rule,
H ooligans shouting,
E verton sunk,
L eeds yuck,
S houts and screams everywhere,
E verton 0, Chelsea 4,
A ims, shoots, *scores!*

Anthony Parratt (11)
Hatch Warren Junior School

The Monster From The Woods

As the moon reaches height
A scurry, a bustle, a flick
A distant clock strikes midnight
A tail whips away so quick.

Away in the blackened dark
With evil, yellow eyes
Hiding in the rusty bark
The evil monster flies.

With its massive claws
And rustled up wings.
It opens its giant jaws,
Hoping for breakfast and things.

A little mouse pricks his ears,
Frightened, scared, timid.
The devil quickly hears
And strikes before he's hidden.

The owl spreads his wings
And flies into the dark
Claws closed like rings
And a distant dog barks.

Victoria Steventon (10)
Hatch Warren Junior School

The Blobles

The Blobles are green
Fuzzy things that fly in the night,
When they land they give you a terrible fright.
Lastly, naughty and ghostly things
Live in the forest where the Blobles
Wait for you and me.

Jake McDermott (11)
Hatch Warren Junior School

Shark

G reatest killer of the ocean
R egretting nothing at all.
E ating away at countless fishes
A ferocious death machine
T error to the seas.

W hooshing through the water
H ead a sign of fear
I n the murky darkness
T railing blood and destruction
E verywhere he goes.

S liding through the darkness
H iding is no use against
A master of surprise.
R eaching out with jaws like steel
K iller in the waves.

Beth Smith (10)
Hatch Warren Junior School

There Once Was A Monkey

There once was a monkey
With a KitKat Chunky,
Swinging on vines
With a tin of Heinz.
He spilled the beans
About his jeans.
He had some Mars,
He's obsessed with chocolate bars.
He had some cheese
But was chased by bees.

Alex Smith (10)
Hatch Warren Junior School

Bob The Mouse!

Bob the mouse
Lived in the most peculiar house!
Every day, all through the night,
The two cats hissing, having a fight.

So Bob went out
And made a doubt,
That any other place
Wouldn't be a disgrace.

So he packed and packed
And packed and packed,
It was mostly cheese
That made him so fat!

He found a car,
A mini Porsche,
It was definitely
Faster than a horse.

He went to the casino,
Found £1 million.
'You cheated,'
Said his friend, Maximillion.

So he jumped in a 'copter
And flew away fine,
But then came the copstas,
Right behind!

He jumped out the 'copter
And landed in his car,
He put in the key
And drove away far.

Soon he got home
And said, 'That's nice!'
The cats then killed him
Like some tiny woodlice!

Alex Miles (10)
Hatch Warren Junior School

Animals

H orses,
O riginal,
R iding,
S tallion,
E nergetic.

T igers,
I ntelligent,
G rowling,
E ating animals,
R est now,
S leep.

C uddly
A nd
T iny,
S weet.

M ice,
I nnocent,
C ute,
E legant.

D ragons,
R aging flames,
A ttack,
G ulp down prey,
O ff the ground,
N ow
S oaring in the air.

P andas,
A ttacked by people,
N ow, run,
D anger,
A ttack them,
S afe.

Becky Stevenson (11)
Hatch Warren Junior School

How To Make Enemies

You will need: a bowl, a whisk, a blender, 1 teaspoon.

Ingredients: 10 grams of tricks
               5 grams of prettiness
              20 grams of anger
              60 grams of horribleness
              40 grams of hate
              50 grams of lies.

Put in your bowl 10 grams of tricks and 5 grams of prettiness
Whisk carefully, then get 20 grams of anger
Mix with 2 cups of water then whisk.
Then get 3 teaspoons of sugar
And 40 grams of hate, whisk carefully.
Then get 60 grams of horribleness and 50 grams of lies
And blend for 2 minutes.
Leave for 3 minutes then put in oven for 30 minutes.
When cooked leave for 10 minutes.

What to do with your enemy cake:
Give it to a nice, neat child who you hate
Then let it do the rest.

Your cake will turn into a bully and will hurt and upset
That small child until she's 20.

Jade Levene-Endfield (11)
Hatch Warren Junior School

The Dragon

The dragon up in north, so tall,
Leans on his castle wall.
He breathes out fire, flames that burn,
And he says, 'Just wait your turn.'

But then at midnight he screams and shouts,
He ferociously jumps about.
But then, one night, all goes quiet,
Because the dragon's on a diet.

Cerri Griffiths (11)
Hatch Warren Junior School

There's A Monster At The End Of My Bed!

There is a thing, that comes in my room,
Which lounges at the end of my bed.
I get really scared,
I really only want my ted,
Its shadow stands right over me,
I can see its lips move.
As I can see
Its eyes are dark, its hair is green.
It's like my mum with her shower cap on,
No glasses on.
Please don't hurt me.
Ooh I won't.
Goodnight Jack.
Goodnight Mum,
But I'm sure it will be back tomorrow night.

Sarah-Jane Osgood (10)
Hatch Warren Junior School

Football Poem

C ardiff rule
A cting fools
R eading are rubbish
D own in the dumps
I celand win
F or the World Cup
F orgetting England who lose again.

C helsea lose
I n the relegation zone
T elford are great
Y ears to come.

Owen Slade (10)
Hatch Warren Junior School

Animals

C ute
A nd
T iny

D opey
O ld
G entle

T errible,
I ntelligent.
G reat,
E normous.
R ainforest

D iving,
O ver.
L iving,
P eacefully.
H igh,
I n,
N everland.

G rass-eating animal.
U nder the bench,
I n the hutch.
N udge, nudge, nudge.
E ating
A way.

P atch
I s
G reat!

Hannah Russell (10)
Hatch Warren Junior School

Crazy Footie

A cting Ambrosio
B rill Becks
C urling Carlos
D onkey Davids
E xcellent Emerson
F unky Fergie
G roovy Galas
H ealing Henry
I diot Ince
J umping Jay-Jay
K ool Kleberson
L ittle Lizarrazu
M agic Mutu
N utty Neville
O dd Owen
P uka Phillips
Q uick Quinn
R unning Ronaldo
S uper Smith
T opnotch Teddy
U gly Upson
V ictorious Vaselle
W inner Watson
X treme Xavier
Y ellow Yaken
Z ooming Zidane.

Sean Hawkins (10)
Hatch Warren Junior School

Loving

I love you in the morning,
I love you in the night,
I love you in the darkness
And unflattering light,
I love you when you're sleeping,
I love when you're awake,
I love you when you're nauseous,
Because you've eaten too much cake,
(Burp!) Whoa!
I love you when you're sickly,
I love when you feel fine,
I love you all around the world,
I love you all the time,
I love you all the time.

Charlie Tilbrook (10)
Hatch Warren Junior School

An Apple Poem

A healthy munch,
P er month
P lus a banana or two.
L isten to your doctor,
'E 'll tell you!

C ores of an apple, pips of an
O range.
R eally healthy eating
E quals a
S tupendously healthy life.

Ashleigh Williams (11)
Hatch Warren Junior School

Cars, Cars

Cars, cars, so many of them,
All as shiny as a gem.
Ferrari 360 is the best,
I might have to give it a test.

Bugatti Veyron so much speed,
When it comes past you'll drop to your knees.
Then comes along a BMW M3,
So excited I just hit a tree!

The fastest car is a McLaren F1,
But now look, the Bugatti just spun!
Then comes along a Ford Fiesta,
Think he's the besta!

Then comes past a Ferrari F40,
Looking a bit naughty.
This is the end,
I hope it didn't drive you round the bend.

Craig Sims (10)
Hatch Warren Junior School

My Horse

Mane swaying, legs galloping.
Head tossing, hooves bucking.
Riding away into the distance.
Mouth chomping, tongue slurping.
Rolling in the mud!
Tree trunk, have to jump.
Happy still, funny feel.
Running, jumping, moving, laying.
Gentle as they come!

Hollie Cobbett-Payne (10)
Hatch Warren Junior School

Shooting Stars

Shooting stars
Glazing through
The bedroom window
Awakening the *dead* . . .

Comes to the forest
And all you can hear is
Hoot, hoot
But not an owl
Something strange
Comes near to you
Run . . .

Katie Sims (10)
Hatch Warren Junior School

My Family

My dad's got a Ferrari
A Mazda too,
My mum's a pop singer
And only 22,
My brother's a pro footballer
He's a millionaire,
He plays in England's first squad
And always changes his hair.
So welcome to my family,
Please grab a chair.
They're all really famous,
So just sit and stare.

Michael Cheng (10)
Hatch Warren Junior School

Creatures Of The World

E xciting places to go
N ice little creatures.
V icious traps set out.
I gnorant people eat them.
R ich people fox hunt
O r people ruin their homes.
N ice people save the creatures,
M ean people catch the creatures.
E nsure that you save the creatures,
N ice little creatures aren't vicious,
T ry to help them!

Elliot Parker (11)
Hatch Warren Junior School

Night-Time

At night-time
Cats screech,
Sirens echo through the night,
So you get into bed
And you turn out the light,
Nobody knows what goes on in the night!

Tanya Reap (11)
Hatch Warren Junior School

Recipe For Woods

1 A sprinkle of seeds
2 A layer of mud
3 A splash of water
4 A few creepy-crawlies
5 Leave to grow
6 Stick a few green leaves on top.
   Ready to look at!

Tom Baker (10)
Hatch Warren Junior School

School

People say school is cool,
But I don't think it is at all.
It's just so boring,
                        Boring,
                                Boring,
Kids complain cos of all my snoring.
All you do is plain old writing,
Kids in the playground always fighting.
People laughing, giggling, prancing,
But I don't feel like silly dancing.

Annabelle Tripp (10)
Hatch Warren Junior School

Nonsense Poem

In the Himalayas it's snowing,
In Africa it's cold,
In Wales it's boiling hot,
In Iceland the ice has gone.

In the Sahara Desert it's pouring,
In India it's a blizzard,
In the North Pole it's over 200 degrees,
In England it's the monsoon season.

Maddie Higgins (10)
Hatch Warren Junior School

My Class And Me

Mikey is always green,
    Yazmin is always mean,
Charlie is always reading,
    Lisa is always dreaming,
Annie is always fighting,
    Sam is always writing,
So me, I'm just me!

Lizzie Hall (11)
Hatch Warren Junior School

My Poor Cake

Oh dear, oh dear,
I dropped my cake
All over the floor for goodness sake,
It's over here, it's over there,
I'm looking around, it's everywhere.

Oh dear, oh dear,
What have we here?
It's on my mum's new top,
Maybe I should run away
And never ever stop!

Danielle Neeve (10)
Hatch Warren Junior School

Who Am I?

Math adder
Number basher
Puzzle crasher
Sum thrasher
Problem masher
Division smasher
Fraction beater
Battery eater
Who am I?

James Pemberton (10)
Hatch Warren Junior School

Footie Crazy

Here comes Beckham, running down the wing
He looks so posh, like he was a king.
The ref put up a red,
As the crowd went to bed,
The Arsenal manager cries,
As the crowd dies.

Kyle Savidge (10)
Hatch Warren Junior School

Hattle Dumpling

Hattle Dumpling,
Fell off the stall.

Went outside,
Then kicked the wall.

She left the house,
Then sat on a wall.

She then fell off,
Now doesn't exist at all.

Charlotte Nuttall (11)
Hatch Warren Junior School

Mrs Peck Peck

Mrs Peck Peck goes pecking for bread,
Bob, bob, bob goes her little round head,
Tame as a pussy cat in the street,
Peck, peck, peck goes her little yellow beak,
With her little yellow beak and her little round head
Mrs Peck Peck goes pecking for bread.

Katherine Roberts (10)
Hatch Warren Junior School

Lazy Cat

L azy cat, lazy cat,
A lways sleeping, never
Z ooming around,
Y awning all the time.

C ats are fluffy,
A lways cleaning,
T o keep their fur so soft.

Lisa Cristofoli (10)
Hatch Warren Junior School

Beaches

Rocky, sandy, sunny beaches,
With rock pools,
Shells and the
Glistening, shimmering sea.

Everyone comes
To play
In the sea
On a hot sunny day.

At the day's end
To cool down
Dip in the
Cold sea!

Alice Wills (10)
Hatch Warren Junior School

Icarus Dun

Here lays the body of
Icarus Dun
Fell to his death
Flew too close to the sun.
RIP.

Ricky Stevens (9)
Hatch Warren Junior School

I Saw A Bear!

I saw a bear over there,
I could not stop to stand and stare,
I did not dare to go in there.
Fiddled with my hair.
Why God, it's just not fair!
Why don't I have the courage to go in there?

Barnaby Duff (10)
Hatch Warren Junior School

The Mind-Boggling Voice

It just won't go,
That voice in my head,
I've tried to get rid of it but I'm in trouble instead.
Oh I just wish it would go,
That mind-boggling thing
Just go, go, go
Or I will do something bad
So mind your steps you disgraceful thing
Otherwise you will be in trouble!

Michael Woods (10)
Hatch Warren Junior School

Dragons

Dragon in the mist
Roaring
It was pouring
Trees moan in pain
Bones crunch
The dragons munch.

Matthew Flain (9)
Hatch Warren Junior School

My School

My school is very tall,
My school is as long as shopping mall,
My school is very dusty,
As dusty as a rug,
That makes my school the very best.

Ella Hardy (8)
Hatch Warren Junior School

Dinner Time!

I make a house under the table
and play there wherever I'm able.
I've got a cooker and a book,
sit right down and take a look.
I've got some cups and a plate
Teddy's hungry and he won't wait.
Now it's tea time, Mum says stop
my dinner's waiting on the table top.

Tunisa Dean (10)
Hatch Warren Junior School

Frog

Fly stopper
Lillipad hopper
Swamp swimmer
Grime trimmer
Pond liver
Near river.

Jay Scarsbrook (10)
Hatch Warren Junior School

Sparky The Spaniel

Can you say no to his cute little eyes?
Doesn't he look adorable even when he lies!
Can you send him out when it's raining?
Doesn't he look sweet when he sits there waiting?
Sparky's so special he's my miniature puppy!
Sometimes I think he's got the mind of a guppy.

Lisa Robertson (10)
Hatch Warren Junior School

Monster Crawls

'Time for bed,' Mum calls,
That's when the monster crawls.
'What's the matter?' Mum will say,
'Argh! there's a monster in my way!'
I'll jump on my bed,
Oh look there's Uncle Ted.
'Why are you on the bed?'
'Shut up!' is what I said!
'Look over there.'
'Oh yeah, a bear.'
'No that's a monster silly!'
'No, that's just Lilly!'

Danielle Clarke (11)
Hatch Warren Junior School

Please!

Aww, Mum please,
How can you leave that?
Aww Mum please,
It's just a little bit of fat!

Aww Dad please,
I really wanna puppy!
Aww Dad please,
He looks like a guppy!

Aww Gran please,
I don't wanna fish!
Aww Gran please,
Oh I wish, I wish, *I wish!*

Hannah Murphy (10)
Hatch Warren Junior School

My Recipe For A Perfect Class

You will need: I teaspoon of tidiness,
20 well-behaved children,
10 badly-behaved children,
1 stressy teacher,
A sprinkle of talent and ½oz of intelligence.

1 Mix the tidiness and children together
adding the intelligence gradually.

2 Add the stressy teacher and leave to cook
for 6½ hours a day.

3 Finally sprinkle the talent on top
and leave to cool.

Rory Bethell (11)
Hatch Warren Junior School

How To Make A Bubbly Parent

Ingredients: 2 ounces of love
3 ounces of cleanliness
2 ounces of bad-tempered kids
4 minutes in the oven
5 in the fridge
3 minutes to cool, then ready to live.
2 ounces of oldness.

When you are done with life
You give the recipe to your kids.
For generations to come, they'll give it to their kids
And so on during life.

So all parents will be bubbly
For yours and mine, time after time.

Imogen O'Callaghan (10)
Hatch Warren Junior School

5 Reasons Why!

'You're going to school
even if you cry
if you don't want to go
give me five reasons why?'

'1 It's boring,
2 I don't know anything
3 The teachers are horrid,
4 I get too much homework,
5 I have to go to detention.'

'You make it boring,
you know lots,
the teacher's nice,
you've never had homework
in your whole, entire life!
What about the detention bit?
Don't even mention it!'

I got to school
but I was late
I got a detention
I was feeling faint.

My mum grounded me
I said, 'No way!'
So I had to go to school
every . . . single . . . day!

Sam Lance (11)
Hatch Warren Junior School

My Horror World

Dark and damp
Cruel and evil
One step and death . . . is nearing
Around there's no one
I'm alone
 . . . All alone in my head.

Tanya Welton (10)
Hatch Warren Junior School

Thirty Lines

She expects me to write a poem.
A poem!
Thirty lines she said.
I mean that's got to be impossible.
Thirty lines,
Thirty whole lines.
No way!
I can't write poems to save my life,
I can't even do shape poems,
Or an acrostic.
Oh this is ridiculous,
Everyone else is writing
And I'm just sitting here,
Just sitting here,
Fiddling with my pencil.
Doodling on the table,
Oops! Shouldn't have said that,
Never mind,
Won't get in trouble if the teacher doesn't know.
Oh hurry up!
Someone has to finish soon,
I'm so bored.
I've spent so long waiting,
I've made up my own song.
Really I did.
Do you want to hear it?
Thirty lines,
Thirty lines,
All she said was . . .
Thirty lines!

Jessica Sandwell (11)
Hatch Warren Junior School

A Mixed-Up World

If you are to walk
To China and back,
So I've been told
There's a whopping, huge crack!

Inside this hole,
The Prime Minister is a cow,
But snakes can talk and fish can walk
And cats do karate called Miaow!

The towns are quite noisy,
The markets are mad,
The frogs are policemen,
Leaping on people who're bad.

Sheep run the clothes stores,
But I've heard they use their own wool.
There's lots of famous places,
But all the doors you push are marked pull!

In the town centre
The traffic heats up the roads,
While the motorway gets clogged up,
With all its heavy loads.

If you plan to go one day,
Please wear a crafty disguise,
As believe it or not,
The animals in the cities have very keen eyes.

So if you are to walk
To China and back,
So I've been told,
There's a whopping, huge crack!

Philip Hughes (10)
Hatch Warren Junior School

Monsters

Big, slimy, all hair,
Go and see him if you dare!
Nine times your height,
Watch out he might bite!

Small, wet, shy,
Watch out, you might die!
Coming round that corner . . . 'Boo!'
He scared you!

Big with a wig,
Watch him dig.
Making your grave,
In his secret cave!

Matthew Potter (11)
Hatch Warren Junior School

Cobra

Hi, the name's Cobra, King Cobra
I've got a deadly sting
I may cause a big marking
I may cause a row
Because I scared them right now!

I'm the deadliest snake in the Wild West,
I eat birds out of their nest.
I'm all slimy and long,
If you get attacked just sing me a song!

Kieron Fuller (10)
Hatch Warren Junior School

The Moon

The moon is like a glowing unicorn
Galloping in the sky.

The moon is like a gleaming mirror
Reflecting in the deep blue sea.

The moon is like a beaming face
Smiling at the stars.

The moon is like a dazzling white cat
Running with the birds.

The moon is like a huge snowball
Thrown out into space.

The moon is frosty and cold
Where dreams come true.

Martha Day Cunio (9)
Hiltingbury Junior School

Star Poem

The star of the night
That gleams, beams, twinkles
Trailing its sparkly light behind.
Glowing so bright
You can see it
Through the misty night.
This night
I can see a star
Shining over a stable.
I can see inside
There is a baby boy
Lying on a straw bed.

Sophie Kronenberg (9)
Hiltingbury Junior School

Wind

The wind is like a roaring lion,
Hissing like a tiger,
Howling like an owl,
Barking like a mad dog.

The wind is groaning like a man
With a broken arm,
Roaring like a mad dog,
Wailing like a little baby,
Hissing like a snake.

Lucy Andrews (8)
Hiltingbury Junior School

The Rain Poem

Someone's outside!
He's battering the roof.
He's knocking on the old door.
He's rattling the windows.
He's whooshing down the chimney.
He's watering the plants.
He's making puddles everywhere.

Christian Sillence (8)
Hiltingbury Junior School

The Rain

He flies in the swirling wind
Doing backward flips in tornadoes
Then smashes into the window
And trickles down the pane.

Conor Watson (7)
Hiltingbury Junior School

The Wind

The wind is like a ghost howling loudly.
The wind is like a roar from a lion.
The wind is like a twister.
The wind whirls and it sounds awful.

The trees and the leaves sway gently around.
The acorns roll around on the grass outside.
The squirrels are picking up the acorns from the grass
And the fur is blowing around the place.

Jason Friend (7)
Hiltingbury Junior School

Wind

The wind is like a roaring leopard in the sky.
Barking like a dog,
Crying like a baby.
The wind is dancing in the sky.
Roaring like a tiger,
Whistling like a bird,
Howling like a wolf.

Hannah Bosier (7)
Hiltingbury Junior School

Party Time

It's party time and I'm feeling fine,
I'm going to stay out late with all my mates.
I'm going to dance all night on the dance floor,
I'm going to dance all night until my feet are sore.
While the beats are pumping I'm going to strut my stuff,
I'll keep on rocking until I've had enough.
Don't wait for me I'll be home late
'Cause I'm out partying with all my mates.

Lianne Hyam (10)
Manor Junior School

Junk Food

Chocolate, chocolate, yum, yum, yum,
We like chocolate in our tum,
Milk chocolate, dark chocolate, any kind of chocolate,
We like chocolate yum, yum, yum.

Sweeties, sweeties, crunch, crunch, crunch,
We like sweeties for our lunch,
Small sweeties, big sweeties, any kind of sweeties,
We like sweeties, crunch, crunch, crunch.

Junk food, junk food, you're the best,
You are better than the rest,
Burgers, chips, an ice cream or two,
Junk food, junk food we love you!

Jasmine Stolk (11)
Manor Junior School

Chocolate!

White the lady,
soft the desired
tender and gorgeous
you're in for a surprise!

Dark the widow,
charm, full and mysterious
also tender and careful
full of wisdom, just for you.

Milk the queen,
of them all,
beats fudge and caramel by far!
Let it soak your mind
of its gentle substance!

Lizzie Hogg (10)
Manor Junior School

My Dog

My dog has a funny sense, he can smell fear
And he never sheds a single tear.
His coat is so warm and soft,
He is really afraid of the loft.
His ears are really droopy,
But here and there he decides to have a little poopy.
His tail always wags,
He hates to hear people nag.
He mostly likes to use his eyes
To look at Dad's ties.
His eyes are big and blue
They look shiny and brand new.
He also knows that when he sees us from above,
He is going to be surrounded by love.

Connor Burrows (11)
Manor Junior School

Strike

I strike once, twice, three times an hour.
I'm devilish in a kind of way.
I flaunt my evil wherever I can.
On my journey down to Earth.

I must get this land I say to myself
As I take a short cut down a tree.
I race to the ground (with my pals)
Showing off my energy.

Some people say I'm intrusive,
But I'm merely taking a peek
And it has often been said that I am nature's freak.
Killing's my best hobby.
I'm not an evil force; I'm just doing what I please.

Katherine Bradshaw (10)
Manor Junior School

My Magic Bed

My bed is a wonderful fantasy,
I travel the world at night,
Sometimes I go into space,
Although the aliens give me a fright!

I've watched the children in Africa,
Sleeping out in the cold,
I often drop down food for them
And they eat it as they are told.

I usually visit the waterfall
And watch the sun go down,
This is my favourite place of all,
It never makes me frown.

I'd like to go to China one night,
The outfits are really cool,
But just as I arrive there
I have to get up for school!

Rebecca Ellis (10)
Manor Junior School

School's Out!

School's out, we're gonna have fun
it's a dream come true for everyone.
We're gonna go swimming, gonna play games
we will make use of every day.
We'll go round our friends to have a laugh
then return home for a warm, bubbly bath.
Then when all six weeks have passed
we're back in that old stuffy class.
So that's it, no more fun,
we're back in Hell where we first began!

Michaela Goddard (10)
Manor Junior School

One Winter's Evening

One winter's evening rain began to fall,
Softly then hard and softly again.
Pitter-patter against the window it went,
Like somebody whispering a secret.

The hail then started,
It quite gave me a fright.
Sounded like pebbles being tipped from a bucket onto the roof,
So loud and disturbing.

Out of the window I can see the snow,
Slowly and silently it falls to the ground.
A smooth, white, welcoming yet cold blanket outside,
Waits for me to snuggle into it.

There's a rumble overhead,
It's thunder.
It's like a hungry lion growling,
Beckoning for me to come forward.

Now there's lightning,
It's so bright alongside the black sky.
Purple, blue and yellow,
Lightning is so elegant.

Jasmine Burford (10)
Manor Junior School

Rats

We dash around and make our play,
We fight our foes and run all day.

Chorus
We're the rats, the rats!
Sly diplomats - in baseball caps
We're the rats, the rats!
Unbelievable - aristocrats!

We squeak and grunt all through the town,
We even stole the king's own crown!

Chorus

We scamper quick and scurry slow,
In summer sun or winter snow.

Chorus

We're sharp and quick and on the mark,
We like to fight cats in the park.

Chorus

We hate the dogs and loathe the cats,
And they hate us 'cause we're the rats!

Isobel Richardson (10)
Manor Junior School

Sir Gadabout

Sir Gadabout's my name
Slaying dragons is my game
Because I am a knight
Fighting for what's right
I can move with speed
On my mighty steed
For people in plight
Evil I will fight
For what's right

Sir Gadabout's my name
Saving people made my fame
Because I am a knight
Fighting for what's right
My steed's hooves
Make deep grooves
Morning, noon and night
Nasty creatures I will fight
For what's right

Sir Gadabout's my name
To damsels' help I came
Because I am a knight
Fighting for what's right
I look death in the face
My horse goes at quite a pace
I plunge into darkness to bring light
Evil may be vanquished by my might
Forrrrrrr Whaaaatt's riiiiggghhhtt!

Harrie Mort (10)
Manor Junior School

I Can't Help It, It's The Way Of Life!

I'm running fast,
My pulse is going down at last,
I can hear the music of a thrush,
The sweetness you can't crush,
I taste the food that is brought to me,
I can't help how I react,
I see the world change every day,
Nothing good can last,
It's Earth's way.
I feel the love in my mother's heart,
As she cuddles me with all her love,
I write her a card,
To tell her what she means to me,
I take a whiff of the sweet meringue,
I taste the lemon with a slight tang,
My blood is pumping through my veins,
It helps my heart go thud . . .
I can't help it, it's the way of life!

Tilly Besant (10)
Manor Junior School

Why?

'Go on, leave without a trace,' all the kids would say,
With a look of sadness on her face she'd slowly walk away.
At school we wondered where she'd gone, the teachers wouldn't say,
But the look upon their faces showed that all was murky and grey.
Maybe she'd just hurt herself, an accident in a car,
Or maybe even a sadder thing,
No we never pushed her that far.
An announcement in assembly proved my theory true,
No longer was she on this earth, so lonely and so blue.
Now I know what happened,
She couldn't take any more.
If I'd known what she was going through
I would have stopped for sure.

Laura Randell (11)
Manor Junior School

Baton Twirling

Pick up a baton, twirl it around,
Watch out! it may fall to the ground,
Flick of your thumb,
You'll never be glum,
Figure of eight,
Teacher's a good mate,
It's always fun at twirling.

Dress up in leotards,
Pink, white and blue,
In front of a judge,
I'm as scared as you,
The comp is over, get ready to wait,
I'll tell you, you've made no mistakes,
Look out! look out! he's called your name!
Well done, well done, you've done it again!

Jordan Roberts (10)
Marycourt School

The Ginger Cat

The colour of a ginger cat is marmalade
He always comes to your aid

A ginger cat has a very good brain
People never call ginger cats insane

A ginger cat never has a straight back
He always stops by for a snack

A ginger cat stands guard of a pram
I always feed him some ham.

James Morgan (11)
Marycourt School

I Don't Know What My Pet Is Called

I don't know what my pet is called!
He's not resourceful at all.
He is a pain cos he is so lame.

He has a friend in Afghanistan
And he also thinks he's Superman.
He looks like a toadstool but he's not
He also has a head that rots.

I don't know what my pet is called
I don't know what he is.
All I know is I found him in a dizz.
He does not know how to do acrobats
Then I found out he was just a cat!

Yiannis Panou (8)
Marycourt School

Dolphin

Dolphins are graceful in the sea,
They move around swiftly,
As gentle as can be,
Dolphins are nice, they mean no harm,
They may be extinct soon,
The poor little things,
They're found on the shore,
Been washed up by the sea,
We're trying to help them,
But it makes no difference,
Soon it will be over,
Soon they will be gone.

Josephine Durham (11)
Marycourt School

My Gorgeous Bedroom

I have a bedroom, its ceilings slope like hills,
I have a bedroom, its walls are perfectly pink,
I have a bedroom where maniac brothers are not allowed to go!
I have a bedroom, it has amazing pop star posters,
I have a bedroom where you can see the Isle of Wight out the back,
I have a bedroom full of beautiful ballerinas,
I have a bedroom which is incredibly neat and tidy,
I have a bedroom with stylish make-up,
I have a bedroom with cunning books,
I have a bedroom with gorgeous bags,
I have a bedroom with cute and cuddly toys,
I have a bedroom with a cool karaoke machine,
I love my bedroom!

Charis White (8)
Marycourt School

The Owl

Everywhere I see,
Something up there in that tree,
Big round eyes,
No ears,
But it never cries with proper tears,
I never know what it is up there,
But sometimes it gives me a scare,
It has feathers dark and fair,
Now I know it's an owl up there.

Caroline Musto (9)
Marycourt School

Sports

I like playing sports,
There's so many to choose,
As long as you try your best,
It doesn't matter if you lose.

I like playing tennis,
Once a week on Tuesday,
Lobs, volleys, smashes,
It's fun all the way.

I also do kickboxing,
It's very hard sometimes,
Stretches, kicks and punching,
But at the end you feel fine.

Jack Curtis (8)
Marycourt School

Quiet

A feather fell to the ground,
Not a sound.
A bee in your ear,
You can't hear.
A plant growing I can't hear,
Oh dear!
I've got supersonic ears,
For all those years,
Don't you worry,
You'll be sorry.

Alexander Morrison (8)
Marycourt School

Happiness

Happiness is when you are near the ones you love,
Happiness is the sound of laughter,
Happiness is a glimpse of good,
Happiness is being loved.

Happiness is a bright, sunny day,
Happiness is playing with friends and family,
Happiness is a glimpse of bright colour.

Ben Lewis (9)
Marycourt School

Hearing

I can hear the gentle breeze,
I can hear the flowers sprouting,
I can hear the dust floating in the air,
I can hear the stars glowing in the sky,
I can hear cats hiding in the dark,
I can hear the calm sea at the beach,
I can hear the living dead under my feet,
I can hear the moon sleeping,
I can hear the sun rising,
I can hear a drop of blood from miles away.

Thomas Battersby (8)
Marycourt School

Morning

Morning is the start of the day,
Morning is peace,
Morning is the sunlight,
Morning is getting ready
And that's why I like morning.

Imogen Langton (8)
Marycourt School

My Cat

I have a very happy cat,
Smartie is her name,
At night she prowls around outside,
In the morning sleeping is her game.

She loves to run and chase the birds,
Blackbirds, robins and blue tits,
But if she ever saw a snake,
She would probably lose her wits!

Smartie is very fluffy,
She likes a lot of fuss,
But if you tickle her belly too much
She becomes an angry puss.

My tabby has a funny habit,
She likes to drink out of the sink,
Mum has caught her more than once,
Dipping in the toilet for a drink.

When the weather's bad and stormy outside
And Smartie has been in for hours,
We show her the door,
She wants to go out no more
And hides in the corner and cowers,

That's my cat . . .

Harvey Meeds (9)
Marycourt School

The Adventures Of Conor

Conor met a large witch,
Her voice was at a terrible pitch.
The witch had jagged rotten teeth,
She was a very good thief.
'Hello Conor, what a nice leg,
I could eat that with an egg.'
Conor, Conor didn't shout,
He opened his gel up and spiked his hair up,
Then silently gobbled her up.

Conor met a scary nurse,
Conor, Conor didn't hide in his purse.
She had a big scary pill,
Conor thought he could chill.
The nurse said, 'How nice to meet you,
Now I shall drug you.'
Conor, Conor didn't shout,
Conor didn't wail or call out.
He opened his gel up and spiked his hair up
And Conor squeezed the nurse in a cup.

Conor met a big, fat bully,
Conor, Conor wasn't scared fully.
The bully had an ugly face
And had a bright silver brace.
The bully said, 'Nice glasses,
I'll snap them so you can't go to the classes.'
Conor, Conor didn't shout,
Conor, didn't call out.
Conor bellowed, 'Leave me alone,
Otherwise you'll wish you had a clone.'

Jason Wakley (11)
Mill Rythe Junior School

There's A Monster In My House

Monster going round my head,
It's hiding in the curtain
And underneath my bed.
I'm sitting in my bed,
I feel a shiver down my spine,
Monster comes and says, 'You will be mine.'

I screamed for my mum and dad,
They came just like that,
Oh why be so scared, it's only a toy bat.

I checked all around my house,
But my brother did not care
If it lived in the cupboard
Or underneath the stairs.

I looked in the kitchen,
Incase it ate some food.
My brother said if he found it
He would call it Dude.

I found a headless monster
In my bed last night,
It was not me who was scared,
It had a fright.

It was a friendly monster,
He was not even dead,
It was a shame he could not talk,
Because he had no head!

Isabel Wellbelove (11)
Mill Rythe Junior School

Holly The Golden Retriever

Eyes as brown as a chocolate bar,
My dog's number one by very far.

Her fur so fluffy and white as snow,
My dog's so playful and I love her so.

She rolls around in the muddy grass,
After we've given her a nice clean bath.

We take her for walks along the seaside,
I throw out a stick and she swims in the tide.

We take her home and dry her off,
Even though she smells a bit over the top.

Frankie Jacobs (11)
Mill Rythe Junior School

St Bernard's

(In memory of my dog Bruno)

Trudging softly in the snow,
Tails wagging to and fro.

Fur as fluffy as a cloud,
Panting is so very loud.

Hunting around the icy mountains,
Icicles look like frozen fountains.

Digging up the frosted snow,
Rescuing people from down below.

They wear a barrel around their neck
Containing brandy for the rescued wreck.

Louise Wallis (11)
Mill Rythe Junior School

As She Looks

As she looks through a classroom window,
Why does she stare into nothing?
Her thoughts following the wind,
Drifting away into the clouds.

I must say I know her well,
But I still question her.
I know she wants to catch a cloud,
Or sit in a meadow among flowers.

Every day she will sit by a willow tree, dreaming,
I know all this as she is me.
My dream is to fly among the birds,
Maybe one day, I will.

Hannah Mead (10)
Mill Rythe Junior School

Noise

The swaying of trees,
The voices of a crowd,
The wind in the air,
The music that's loud.

The roaring of tigers,
The bark of a dog,
The purring cat,
The snort of a hog.

The creaking stairs,
All in the house,
The stamping feet,
The squeak of a mouse.

Zoe Stockton (11)
Mill Rythe Junior School

My Pet Tarantula

His 8 furry legs
Scuttle round all day,
But when it comes to night-time
He no longer wants to play.

His name is Percy
And I've had him all my life.
He's had 4 babies
But he hasn't got a wife.

One day he went missing,
He did not return that night.
We searched the house and garden
But he still wasn't in sight.

One month later
There came a knock at the door.
Someone had saved Percy
And we're as happy as before.

Alex Woolhouse (11)
Mill Rythe Junior School

Fire Is . . .

Fire is an argument progressing with anger and hate,
Fire is burnt food giving the taste of cold hearted war,
Fire is anger waiting for water to calm it down,
Fire is a new home with a new scent to live with,
Fire is cold metal, beautiful in its own mind,
Fire is an empty building with no one else but them,
Fire is like your empty feeling filling up your tears.

Shannon Cross (11)
Mill Rythe Junior School

Hunted

Running, running,
I have to get away.
It's poachers with their sticks and guns,
I have to get away.

Help me, help me,
Someone help me please.
In my mind,
I see my mother pounding right next to me.

Silence, silence,
'Is it safe?' I say.
I'm out of breath,
I need a rest.

I close my eyes
And count to ten.
Then soon, soon,
I would be home again.

Kate Pearson (11)
Mill Rythe Junior School

Fire Is Like . . .

Fire is a mixture of colours in a special arrangement,
Fire is a red-hot chilli burning in your mouth,
Fire is like a new beginning for everyone,
Fire is like a volcano melting everything,
Fire is like the burning inside when you're angry,
Fire is the sun setting on the land,
Fire is as hot as the sun,
Fire is a sending from the gods above.
Fire is this poem.

Hannah-Louise Martin (11)
Mill Rythe Junior School

Nature

Rabbits springing along the ground,
Squirrels chasing each other up the trees.
Birds singing sweet little songs,
Foxes sleeping in their dens.

Grass blowing in the wind,
Flowers sprouting all around.
Trees throwing their leaves away,
Bushes with berries and prickles too.

The howling wind making me shiver,
The scorching sun taking off my jumper.
The white snow gleaming in the sun,
It's starting to rain now, I think I'll go home.

Sian Medlow (11)
Mill Rythe Junior School

A Baby

My mum's having a baby
And I don't know what to think.
Will it become close to me
Or pull my hair and bite?
Will it look just like my mum
Or be just like my dad?
Will it live life to the full
Or be a total drag?
Will they be a geek at school
Or be the coolest one?
I still don't know what to think,
Maybe I will have a shock.
There's one thing I do hope,
What I really, really hope,
Is that they will like me!

Hannah Hickman (11)
Mill Rythe Junior School

What Am I?

Swimming in the golden sea,
Looking round at you and me,
Diving in the coral reef,
What am I?
What do you see?

I am purring on a chair,
Climbing on rooftops as a dare,
Miaowing on into the night,
What am I?
What is in your sight?

Trotting round in a field,
Neighing for my afternoon meal,
Standing in my stable warm,
Eating up a luscious lawn,
What am I?
What have you seen?

First a fish and then a cat,
Then a pony on a stable mat,
These are the answers,
Did you get them right?
Fish, cat and pony,
Hope you
Got them
In your sight?

Lizzy Noble (11)
Mill Rythe Junior School

The Monkey Who Needed A Wee

There was a monkey who lived in a tree
And one day said, 'I need a wee.'

He searched all night and found some snow,
But didn't find anywhere to go.

Soon he came across a village of people,
He asked them and they looked at the steeple.

He travelled up the millions of stairs,
He got to the top but there was nothing there.

He jumped out of the window and caught fire to his knee
But he still needed to go for a wee.

Suddenly he saw the fire brigade
Who had quickly come to his aid.

Soon the fire was put out,
He was going red and looking about.

Soon he saw a forest and ran in,
He was so desperate he would go in a tin.

He saw a bush and smiled with glee
And finally went to have a wee.

Jennie Davies (11)
Mill Rythe Junior School

The Four Seasons - Tankas

The hot beaming sun
Shines down on us forever,
Winter shan't break through,
We'll try and make winter flee,
Shining sun is all we'll see.

Trees newly budding,
Babies try to take first steps,
Spring has come again,
But what if autumn breaks through,
Then spring is forever doomed.

Darkness takes over,
Autumn leaves fall off the trees
As Dad rakes them up,
Soon the snow shall start to fall
As autumn leaves us for now.

Frozen ponds and lakes,
Snowflakes perching on noses,
Christmas is coming,
We give at this special time.
Now's the end of my tankas.

Cassie Hodgson (10)
Mill Rythe Junior School

Mad House

People cutting their own hair
When they're supposed to be at the fair,
Maaad hoouusse.
When they go through an ordinary door
They think they're going to be in a war,
Maaad hoouusse.
After the pub they are so drunk,
Then they get beaten up by pink haired punks,
Maaad hoouusse.
When they're in their so small bedroom
They think they're a witch and ride a broom,
Maaad hoouusse.
When they're in their big, big kitchen
They think they can do some pinching,
Maaad hoouusse.
They create a stupid dance
Which they have to hold in France,
Maaad hoouusse,
Maaad hoouusse,
Maaaaaaaaaaad hoooouuuusssse.

Robert Cradock (11)
Mill Rythe Junior School

The World

This is my poem today,
This is what I have to say.
Why put men on Mars
Flying through the stars?
Why commit a crime
And spend all your time
In jail?
For you would fail.
Why can't we live without death
And slaughter and theft?
Why do we have war
And make each other poor?
Why hurt each other?
Instead, why don't we be each other's brother,
Try your best
And help the rest.
Don't hold a gun
For it's done,
You're a killer.

Conor Wickham (11)
Mill Rythe Junior School

Singing In France

There was a young man from Nantes
Who liked to skip and dance,
While skipping along
He burst into song
And now he's Top of the Pops in France.

Thomas Mills (10)
Ridgemede Junior School

Travelling With The Queen

The short little queen
In her little white gloves,
After the nursery rhyme
Was scared of the doves.
Up on her horse she gripped the rein,
Suddenly slipped and fell down the drain,
But when she was down there I heard her explain,
'It makes me sick moving along, so
My head starts spinning and singing a song,
I've just been sick, am I insane?
Didn't I tell you I prefer the train?'

Thomas Belfield (9)
Ridgemede Junior School

Absolutely Terrified

I am terrified of the dark,
All these visions in my head
Like the monster in the cupboard
And the one beneath my bed.

And while I'm still awake
The house will moan and groan,
I'm absolutely horror struck
In the dark and all alone.

All my brothers and sisters
Are dreaming (they counted sheep),
But I am just too petrified,
I dare not go to sleep!

Joe Marston (11)
Ridgemede Junior School

Newsflash

Fighting, crying,
Mourning, dying,
Sickness,
Stop.

Bombs, suffering,
Voices, muffling,
Extremists,
Stop.

Politicians have a guess,
Cities in a mess,
Terrorists, conflict,
Stop.

Dreams shattered,
People battered,
Sieges, explosions,
Stop.

Pollution, death,
Have your last breath,
It's still happening,
Stop.

Seen from behind a girl's chador,
All this and more.

Chloe Kellow (10)
Ridgemede Junior School

My School Day

Bogie picking,
Finger flicking,
Clock ticking
All day long.

Children swearing,
Teacher glaring,
Noise blaring
All day long.

Girls writing,
Boys fighting,
Enemies biting
All day long.

It's the end of the day,
Teachers say
Wahey,
It's the end of the day.

Back home
With no moan
Or a groan,
Yesssss.

Tucked up in bed,
Brain's gone dead,
With my ted,
Zzzzzzz.

Liberty Ash-Cutler (9)
Ridgemede Junior School

Parents

Parents are always, well, most of the time, fickle,
If you have plans they could end up in a pickle.
When I tried to go swimming last week,
I ended up climbing a peak.
And take the time they said I could visit a friend,
They made me do chores, it drives me round the bend.
When at last I could go to the theme park,
They got me involved in this 'quilting bee' lark.
When a party with my friends had been set,
They dragged me to the supermarket.
When my parents said I could see a movie,
I ended up at a disco which they thought was groovy.
If my parents are reading this,
Why do they have to give everything a miss?

Hannah Baxter (10)
Ridgemede Junior School

Bathing A Dog

B athing a dog can be very messy
A nd the lovely white towel turns jet-black with mud.
T he azure stains get filthy on the way up,
H e puts paw prints all over the turquoise wall.
I wash him with dog soap,
N ow the soap is washed out,
G et the comb

A nd brush through his long hair for knots.

D on't wear your best white frock,
O w, mind his claws,
G etting out is a bit tricky but it's worth it!

Charlotte Betts (10)
Ridgemede Junior School

Little Star

Little star, little star,
Why don't you burn as bright as me?
Little star, little star,
Why can't you see?

Little star, little star,
Why don't you learn to write?
Little star, little star,
Have you lost your eyesight?

Little star, little star,
Can I turn off the light?
And little star, sleep tight,
Little star, goodnight.

Hannah Fletcher (10)
Ridgemede Junior School

Birthdays

B irthdays are fabulous,
I like them so much.
R unning free from school,
T he holidays are great.
H oping to have a big birthday bash!
D on't do something stupid,
A nd have fun!
Y our birthdays are the best!

Oliver Jeffcott (9)
Ridgemede Junior School

The Fish

There was a fish called Fern,
She was colourful and fast,
The only problem was
She was always last.

Michelle Gibson (10) & Laura Thomas (9)
Ridgemede Junior School

Rockstar Granny

Rockstar Granny looks like a fool,
Rockstar Granny jumping in the hall.
Rockstar Granny head banging on the guitar,
Rockstar Granny she's a superstar.
Rockstar Granny glugged down a pint of beer,
Rockstar Granny she's coming over here.
Rockstar Granny fell on her bum,
Rockstar Granny she's insulting my mum.
Rockstar Granny I know who she is,
Rockstar Granny is my granny Dizz.

Lana Croot (10)
Ridgemede Junior School

What Lies In The Dark?

What lies in the dark
That is greater than a shark?
It must be little creatures
With their own little features.
Is that what lies in the dark
That is greater than a shark?

Hannah Bradbeer (9)
Ridgemede Junior School

Dragon Food

If a dragon lived under the sea
He wouldn't eat you or me
He would eat little fish
On a big, fat, glass dish!

Jack Adamson (10)
Ridgemede Junior School

The Rainbow In The Diamond

When I look at a diamond
I see a rainbow sparkling in the sun,
But when I look again
The storm has just begun.

The next day I come back to this magnificent diamond,
I see the patterns of a tiger,
What a wonderful sight to see.

I see in the diamond waves crashing
And bashing against the rocks.
Oh dear, I see my friends being sucked down a whirlpool.
I see a winter's day, and then I'm called in for tea.
I turn around again
And that's the winter way.

Abbie Veck (9)
Ridgemede Junior School

Butterflies

Butterflies are colourful,
Butterflies are neat,
If you let them fly
They will give you a treat.

Bugs have wings
To help them fly,
If you annoy them
They will be sly.

Bugs are wonderful,
Bugs are quick.
So why don't you see one
Before they're extinct!

Samuel Bennett (9)
Ridgemede Junior School

Swimming

I don't like swimming in the sea,
If you come down with me you'll probably agree.
I don't like it 'cause the water is cold,
If I'm in that sea again I would get sold.

I don't like swimming in a swimming pool,
But bullies and adults will think I'm a fool.
When I'm on a diving board I freeze to stone,
I'd rather be at home giving my dog a big bone.

I don't like paddling in a paddling pool,
My little sister pretends it's a rocky rock pool.
The splashing and sploshing doesn't get the best of me,
Uh oh, Mum's just spilt her peppermint tea.

Annabelle Bench-Elphick (9)
Ridgemede Junior School

Newcastle

N ew football team in the making.
E ntertaining football.
W icked Shearer scoring goals.
C ool football stadium.
A aron Hughes plays left back.
S hearer is the superb captain.
T errific class goals.
L aurent Robert is best at free kicks.
E xcellent players playing.

Josh Barnes & Sam Medhurst (9)
Ridgemede Junior School

The Nine Planets

Uranus, Saturn, Neptune
Are getting married today
Because they're cluttered with rings
So we all shout hooray.

Now Jupiter's the biggest
With its red-hot liquid gas
And Pluto is the smallest
And the ninth planet to pass.

The sun is blazing hot but
For sure not the largest star
Cos there's a bigger one found
In a galaxy so far.

Now Mercury's the hottest
Cos it's right next to the sun
And Mars is next to Earth
It's where Martians come from.

Venus is the one for girls
It's pretty and it's cool
The black hole is the darkest
And is like a space whirlpool.

But we think Earth's the coolest
And it's better than the rest
We can't live on the others
So it's definitely the best.

Sorcha Ingram (10)
Ridgemede Junior School

Grandma

(For my grandmas)

I feel just like a petal
On a red, red rose,
Or a poppy in the rain
Being squirted by a hose.

I feel just like a colour
In a bright rainbow,
Or a lovely satin coat
With a big pink bow.

I feel just like an angel
On a Christmas tree,
Or a small blue wave
In the mighty sea.

I feel just like a smile
In a frowning crowd,
Or the yellow sunshine
Clearing all the clouds.

When I think of you
My feelings are all right,
You make me feel just like a bird
Ready to take flight.

Virginia Faye Sanderson (10)
Ridgemede Junior School

Crazy Classroom

Voices squeaky
Acting freaky
Eyes always leaky
Very cheeky
Feeling peaky
These are the girls
They're very sneaky.

Goal scoring
Lessons are boring
Grouchy morning
Water pouring
Teacher ignoring
These are the boys
They're always snoring.

Head patter
Chitter chatter
What's the matter?
Fly splatter
Homework's scatter
This is the teacher
She's is as mad as a hatter.

Jed Marston (9)
Ridgemede Junior School

In The Winter's Snow

In the winter's
Snow as the breeze
Blows by, whilst the snowflakes
Pass by you, children . . .
Happily making snowmen
Only right behind
. . . you.

It's
Christmas
Day and it's
Time to play . . .
During everyone's . . .
Celebrations, families . . .
Always having fun, just
Like the old . . .
Days!

Sophie Wells (9)
Ridgemede Junior School

I Wish

I wish, I wish I could climb and climb
To the very end of the world.
I wish, I wish I could climb and climb
Until the day goes down again.
I wish, I wish I could fly and fly away.
I wish, I wish I could rule everything.
I wish, I wish there was no school.
I wish, I wish I could go on holiday every day.
I wish, I wish I could be a millionaire.
I wish, I wish I could have some mansions.
I wish, I wish I could have some golden stones.
I wish, I wish I could rule the world.
I wish, I wish I could climb and climb so people were dots
And houses were blocks.
I wish, I wish I could blow up the school.
I wish, I wish all of them,
But I mostly wish I could never die!

Jonathan Walker (9)
Ridgemede Junior School

Trotting

As I walked down the even path to see my horses,
Batty and Geno,
I heard the tweeting calls of the blue tit talking,
I caught a glimpse of my horses walking,
When I came closer I heard them snorting,
I saw the gate string taut,
They saw me doing the saddle sorting.

I saddled up the horses and started off,
We started trotting
And saw Kenny Lotting
Reading a book called 'Animals' by Ted Notting.
We passed a tree we called Totting,
He stood up straight did old Totting,
Then we finished the day by heading back to bed!

Rachael Hill (10)
Ridgemede Junior School

Sea Lovers

Hammerheads smash against the rocks,
The starfish clings onto the rocks,
You can find crabs in the docks,
The divers look at the clocks,
1, 2, 3 splash - divers risk their lives,
They do perfect dives,
They catch nice fish
And sometimes put them in a dish.
Divers are life savers.

Luke Gamblin (9)
Ridgemede Junior School

Octopus, Octopus

'Octopus, octopus where do you live?'
'I live under the water, that's where I live.'
'Octopus, octopus what do you eat?'
'I eat seaweed, that's what I eat.'
'Octopus, octopus what do you hate?'
'I hate sharks, that's what I hate.'
'Octopus, octopus what is that?'
'That is my ink and that is that.'

Hannah Sinclair (10)
Ridgemede Junior School

Sunny Sky

I wonder why the sky is light,
Is it because the sun is bright?
Why is the sun everywhere?
Why is that cloud shaped like a bear?
Is the sun orange or yellow?
I hope you know because I don't know.
Why does the sun shine like a diamond in the sky?
I really do wonder why.

Emma-Jane Deeley (9)
Ridgemede Junior School

The Waterfall

A waterfall
            comes tumbling
            down the hills,
plummeting
      to the
            darkness.
                  Salmon
                  jumping
                              up
                  it,
            ranches
            falling
            d
            o
            w
            n
            it
            until
            it meets
                  the end.

Daniel Pool (9)
Ridgemede Junior School

My Favourite Place

My favourite place is the corner
Of my bedroom,
I like to think there,
Play there
All the time.
Every time I sit in the corner,
I begin to let my imagination
Fill the room,
So there's no more gloom.

Katy Church (9)
Ridgemede Junior School

Sea Breeze

Calm sea coming in,
Waves crashing in the breeze,
Gentle ripples counting them one by one,
Wind coming, waves crashing.

The sand smoothing along the ground,
People watching the sun go down,
Ice creams dropped on a summer's day,
The waves got bigger from today.

The sea started to ripple even bigger,
I started to see pretty coloured shells,
They glistened in the sunlight,
But the sea started to go out and out it's gone.

Helen Harling (9)
Ridgemede Junior School

Almost A Day At The Zoo

Come in and see the animals,
No, the lions won't headbutt you,
They're not going to bite your head off,
Come in and run through the zoo!

The apes do not have pistols
And giraffes won't give you the flu,
So come on in, it's not a sin
To go running through the zoo!

Oh look, it's time to go now,
So run along, scat! Shoo!
I don't know why I even try
To get you to go to the zoo.

Jacob Tudball (10)
Ridgemede Junior School

Sea Storm

Today I hear the waves crashing and bashing
Against the rocks,
Those clumsy waves coming in sharply,
Falling into the water slowly,
Then you'll hear it again and again.

When you look again later you see
The sea getting fainter,
Falling into a deep sleep,
Then you hear it snoring faintly,
Chugging along with all the fish.

Then when it's time for bed
You'll hear the sea shout up at you,
'Sleep little weary head!'

Sophie Huskinson (10)
Ridgemede Junior School

Snow

Thunder roars, lightning claps,
'Oh, oh,' I dropped my hat.
Snowflakes trickle, my nose tickles,
Old Grandpa's indoors eating pickles.
Freezing hands, water like crystal,
Oh poo! I can't use my water pistol.
Snow clumps and crunches,
Delicately lays on tree branches.
People slipping, coats are dripping.
Oh poor birdies must be cold,
Oi that Freddie's a bit bold.
Just thrown a snowball at my head,
Mum just called, gotta go to bed.

Daniel Rao (9)
Ridgemede Junior School

Spaghetti

Spaghetti, spaghetti on a plate,
Spaghetti, spaghetti tastes so great,
Spaghetti, spaghetti in your hair,
Tell your mum she won't care.

Drop your spaghetti on the floor,
Throw the rest at the door,
So when you have spaghetti again,
Next time eat it in your den.

Shannon Biddiss (9)
Ridgemede Junior School

Eight Wishes

I wish that rain clouds never came,
I wish that the sun always shone,
I wish wild animals could be tame,
I wish that all misery was gone.

I wish that life was always fair,
I wish that pain was never real,
I wish that people would show they care,
I wish that damage was quick to heal.

Fiona Haines (9)
Ridgemede Junior School

The Snow Poem

It changes season
To the freezing season of winter.
There's the wintry sky glistening
In the see-through breeze.
The snow's melting bit by bit
When the beautiful sun comes out.
It's melting and melting until
It becomes concrete again.

Liam Hibberd (10)
Ridgemede Junior School

Where I Used To Live

The seaside where I used to live,
My house sitting high on the cliff,
In winter storms rage up
Like an angry dog down by the rocks,
I could see the waves crashing,
It felt like the cliff was moving.

The seaside where I used to live,
My house sitting high on the cliff,
In spring the seas are not so rough,
But the rain starts getting really tough,
I could hear the rain on the roof,
It felt like the cliff was moving.

The seaside where I used to live,
My house sitting high on the cliff,
In summer we could go down to the sea
And buy an ice cream for you and me,
I could smell the whiff of fish and chips,
I felt the lolly as it touched my lips.

The seaside where I used to live,
My house sitting high on the cliff,
In autumn we would play on the sand,
The kite whizzing round and round,
But when I touched the sea with my fingers
I linger hoping to stay.

Eleanor Sammons (9)
Ridgemede Junior School

Wicked Winter

Winter moves on to autumn,
Sees the rusty colours
And frowns.
She changes into her best dress
Of blue and glittering ice
With a crown of diamonds
And high heels of crystal.

She steps out of her palace
And flies over golden fields,
Blowing her cool minty breath
Bringing death.
She shakes her long, white blonde hair
And leaves quiver to the ground.
Trees stand naked and shivering,
Grasses tuck in their heads,
Snowflakes flutter to Earth
And all is white and pure.

Amy He (11)
Rookesbury Park School

Hallowe'en

H eadless horses haunt the town
A nd children scream as witches pass.
L azy goblins come out to play,
L ittle bats eat big fat rats.
O gres growl and stomp around.
W icked witches fly through forests.
E xploding potions make lots of trouble.
E vil elves cast their spells.
N asty vampires suck your blood.

Beatrix Bates (7)
Rookesbury Park School

Wild Winter

Winter has a black cloak of darkness,
You can feel the wind and the starkness.
His character, a contrast of black and white,
Making people shiver day and night.

His limbs are naked branches of a tree,
Frosty breath freezing all he may see,
Great storms he brings and windy gales,
Crying large tears of rain and hail.

He has fun making mayhem and madness,
While we wrap up warm against his coldness.
When winter is over and he melts away
Spring comes out to dance and play.

Georgina Hull (11)
Rookesbury Park School

Spring

Glorious spring glides through the forest,
Kissing the flowers awake.
She wonders when summer will give her a rest
For she thinks that someday she will break.

The flowers are woken by her beauty,
They all dance with so much delight,
The blossoms of trees become ever so fruity.

Hurray! Hurray, here comes summer
To burn away the cold.
All the flowers start to murmur
As she comes forward bright and bold.

Oreva Otobo (11)
Rookesbury Park School

Spring

Spring comes gliding
Through the forest.
She shivers with cold
In the wintry woods.

She kisses each tree in turn
Bringing them to life.
She touches each flower
With her warm hands
And bursts into bloom.

Her long coat
Turns from a deep blue
To a bright green,
Splattered with fresh, bright blooms.

Her long dark hair
Turns to a shimmering blonde
Like sunburst through clouds,
As she steps deeper into the forest.

Spring brings life to all!

Jasmine Riggs-Bristow (10)
Rookesbury Park School

Hallowe'en

H ideous witches fly down from the sky
A nd throw sweets and laugh in anger,
L anding on the ground they chase children,
L eading them away to devilish dungeons.
O ld vicious vampires sharpen their fangs,
W icked skeletons come out of the cupboard.
E vil pumpkins glow in the dark,
E erie grannies scratch and scream,
N asty wizards push children in their cauldrons.

Alistair Main (7)
Rookesbury Park School

The Stroppy Storm

On a stormy night the lightning flashes
And the thunder starts to boom.
On the roof, the hail it lashes,
Overhead clouds start to loom.

The whistling wind begins to howl,
Pounding rain, it goes on crashing.
The fierce lightning scares an owl,
Horrible hail just keeps on bashing.

The wind and sleet, they swirl and whirl,
The clouds are black and grey.
The hurricane does an angry twirl,
The storm is here to stay.

Charlotte Lamb (9)
Rookesbury Park School

Terrible Storms

Rain lashes on the ground
Making such a terrible sound.
Whistling winds make everyone cold
For the storm's voice is big and bold.

Thunder booms dull and deep
While everyone's tucked up asleep.
Lightning brightens up the sky
While little birds they try to fly.

People wrapped up warm inside,
Little children start to hide.
The storm goes on and makes a gale,
Sleet and rain and even hail.

Camilla Longman (8)
Rookesbury Park School

Autumn Ablaze

Autumn strolls with a quiver
Making bodies shake and shiver.
People play through the day
As sunny spirits flow away.

Gently calling winds to blow,
Children know it's time to go.
Swiftly pulling from her pocket
A tiny leaf wrapped around a locket.

Her cloak is a deep crimson red
And she lies on a feathery bed.
Her eyes are a soft, shiny brown
And she wears a golden crown.

Gliding through the rustling leaves,
Sending a sweet gentle breeze.
Flowers falling at her sight,
Turning daylight into night.

Chelsea Hayward (11)
Rookesbury Park School

Wet, Windy Weather

Soft snowflakes fall on the ground,
Snowmen are all around.
A bitter wind blows in my face,
'Let's all have a snowball race.'
Icicles hang from my windowpane,
Look at all that pattering rain.
The paths are full with icy snow,
Nothing colourful can grow.

Minnie Hill-Reid (8)
Rookesbury Park School

Violent Storm

Storm is a very violent fellow,
Lightning that he sends is yellow.
When he speaks thunder booms
And when he shouts lightning zooms.

When he swirls and whirls around
A hurricane occurs on the ground.
His voice is very, very deep
And in the summer he goes to sleep.

When he walks the ground shakes
Causing minor earthquakes.
People all around him scream
As if he was in their worst dream.

Olivia Bowman (9)
Rookesbury Park School

Spring

Spring waves her arms,
And warm breezes chase away the frost,
Her dress, like soft green silk,
She gracefully waves goodbye to winter,
And puts on her flowery crown,
And looks over her new land.

She turns ice into ponds,
And her soft voice wakes animals,
She skips among the new arrivals,
And warms the Earth with her smile,
She jolts the seeds and bulbs to grow,
And makes birds sing with joy.

Lauren Davis (11)
Rookesbury Park School

Hallowe'en

H orrifying hobgoblins scare children to death
A nd witches fly past the moon.
L arge pumpkin pies scoffed up by children.
L ittle slugs leave a silvery slime.
O range ogres stamp and shout.
W izards cast sparkly spells.
E vil vampires' fangs trickle blood.
E erie witches stir their bubbling cauldrons.
N ever go out on Hallowe'en night!

Abigail Guy (8)
Rookesbury Park School

A Trip To Fratton Park

Twenty-two players ready to compete,
Me, my dad, my brother and Kenyo
Gather together with 20,000 other fans.
The players dread being shown the red,
As they come out of the tunnel
The roof lifts from the roar of the fans,
At Fratton Park it always does.
The whistle is blown and the game's underway,
The nightmare of a loss,
The atmosphere great for the club.

Playing football is great as well,
But I wish it was for Pompey,
Agony when the ball hits your face,
Annoyed when it hits the post,
But that's the way it goes,
The feel of the ball when you kick it,
But playing in front of thousands of people
It's more like a dream to me.

Harry Cottle (9)
St Alban's CE Aided Primary School, Havant

War Studies

I go indoors and look at the street,
Burning house and piles of rubble,
I am think about bombing.
I am frightened,
People screaming, we must fight back,
Buried people injured and wounded,
People limping, running and crying.
People sobbing,
I am thinking of bombing.

Loud crashes, droning planes,
Firebombs and loud shouts,
Screeching explosions and concentration camps.
Falling chunks of bombs and planes,
I'm always thinking of bombing.

Elliott Hanan (10)
St Alban's CE Aided Primary School, Havant

Bully

This poem is about me
and all my misery.

You must promise not to tell
about my bullying hell.

It started way back in May
and now it happens every day.

It started with them calling names
and tricking me with their silly games.

And now they think it's funny
to take away my dinner money.

They say if I tell it'll just get worse,
as they laugh at me and take my purse.

Diary I know you will not tell
about my bullying hell.

Connie Bradshaw (9)
St Alban's CE Aided Primary School, Havant

Ali's Barbara

Stay for ages to rehearse,
Script is all in rhyme,
Try to make ourselves heard.

'The prettiest lass between Suez and Scarborough,'
Is the compere's line,
Soon the curtain will open.

A hot city called Old Baghdad
Is the main scene,
In a little house for two.

People wearing different colours,
Some bits of your body can be seen,
Costumes are uncomfortable.

Characters have different attitudes,
My character, Fatima, is not like me,
But some of the others are.

Going behind the scenes is fun,
Where the audience cannot see,
Hiding like a mouse until my entrance.

Tonight's the night that I perform,
It's so exciting I can't keep still,
Saying my lines to the audience I face.

It's all over now,
Acting the play was such a thrill,
As it was such fun, I'm going to audition again!

Emily James (9)
St Alban's CE Aided Primary School, Havant

A Game Of Warhammer

So much death, but fun,
A game, Warhammer.
Tries to overlook
The sadness of war.
It might be exciting,
But has death and destruction
Behind the veil of goodness.
I watch the dice.
They land on a six,
They land on a six,
They land on a six.
They land on a three and a one
And falls to his death, does Saruman.
His Rohirrim strike again and again.
They retreat at the sight of a Cave Troll,
It carves through them like butter
And makes its way towards his heroes.
We come to a shoot phase,
He fires at Lurtz.
Tense moments tick by,
The dice are spinning.
He thinks, *six, six, six.*
I think, *no not that.*
Things are not going well
As Lurtz reels, sways and dies.
My force is diminished to half its number,
I have lost.

Matthew Brook (10)
St Alban's CE Aided Primary School, Havant

Stukas Dive Down

The siren goes off,
The droning begins,
Sheer panic and terror.
Women and children flee
While men in their absence
Turn the key of their plane.

The roar of the engines drowning,
The silent fears of their pilots,
Hearts pounding, pounding
Like the rattle of their rudders.

The Spitfire takes off
And the undercarriage slams closed.
Thoughts of the battle clearly in mind,
Briefly he wonders,
Will I ever see my loved ones again?
He pulls on the yoke to climb higher again.
Thoughts suddenly shattered by the faint
Sight of distant bombers ahead.
He fires his cannons,
An explosion confirms
That one bomber is now dead.

Matthew Gordon (9)
St Alban's CE Aided Primary School, Havant

Stubbington Study Centre

S ea walk was our first activity,
T uck shop was great,
U seful advice was given,
B adgers as cute as can be,
B rilliant food,
I ndoor and outdoor activities,
N ights were very long,
G reat friends were made,
T ons of fun,
O h no to any rules,
N oisy children that's us!

S ong contest was won by Drey,
T ime passed too quickly,
U ltimate fun was what we had,
D ropped off to sleep at night,
Y ou all had fun whoever you were.

C onservation area was huge,
E ggs were eaten for breakfast,
N atural environment,
T rees about the place,
R ight place to be,
E xcitement all around.

Nardia Bell (10)
St Alban's CE Aided Primary School, Havant

Night In Bed

At night sat in bed,
I see a black and yellow head.
Round the corner off he goes,
Gets his men and starts to row.
Then my mum and dad ask,
'Are you doing some noisy task?'
I reply and say,
'No, no it is the end of the day.'
I shut my eyes and go to sleep,
I feel as though I am in a heap.
I wake up and think of World War II,
I think of those people I hardly knew,
Who got hurt and weren't even alert,
So I think about monsters and goo.
I think of those people I hardly knew,
And all they thought about was their loved ones
And all those people who lost their sons.
So all those monsters and gobbley goo
I still think of those people I hardly knew.

Charlie Knight (10)
St Alban's CE Aided Primary School, Havant

Gondor

The men
weak feathers
floating in fear
watch
as Orcs climb
ladders and walls
like giant spiders.

Men
have no hope
and retreat like
scattering ants
who will die very soon.

Peter Vermeulen (11)
St Jude's CE Primary School, Portsmouth

The Elephant

The big, grey beast
Tramples through the jungle
Mowing it down,
A lawn mower
Swishing its tail with its skinny, teeny-weeny hairs.

Chopping down the trees
With its singing, shining tusks in the African sun.
The thirsty car driving down to the waterhole,
Swishing its tail with its skinny, teeny-weeny hairs.

The long, grey hose
Squirting water at everything in its way.
The big, listening fans
Cooling down the grey beast's body,
Swishing its tail with its skinny teeny-weeny hairs.

Alice Evans & Jon Aspden (11)
St Jude's CE Primary School, Portsmouth

Hamsters

Runs in its ball
All day long.
A tiny bundle of fun but
It sleeps in the day
And wakes in the night.
Round and round it goes
In its wheel.
In its wheel making a terrible noise,
Starts to wake the neighbours.

Lewis O'Brennan (11) & Daniel Davies (10)
St Jude's CE Primary School, Portsmouth

Defending The Wall

Men await the massive assault,
What do they see?
The Orcs - little dots in the distance
Look no threat.

What else do they see?
Black shadows of the Ringwraiths
Blanket the ground,
Threatening the men of Gondor.

Archers shoot,
Spearmen throw,
Gondor is out-numbered
By loads.

The battering ram comes to the gate,
The reinforcements are too late.
The world of men is over,
The time of the Orcs has come.

Jake Camburn (10) & Jacob Welch (11)
St Jude's CE Primary School, Portsmouth

Ronaldo Cinquain

Football
Hat-trick heroes
Ronaldo scores again
Beckham scores for Real Madrid
Hurray!

George Brundish (10)
St Jude's CE Primary School, Portsmouth

My Friend

I once thought I'd tell my friend
The truth of what she was.
She criticised my opinion
And thought she was the boss.
    My friend!
        My friend!

I once thought I'd tell my friend
Where we'd go tonight.
She didn't agree with me
And then we got into a fight.
    My friend!
        My friend!

I once thought I'd tell my friend
How much she meant to me.
She blushed and blushed
And for once agreed with me.
    My friend!
        My friend!

Hannah Leslie & Danielle Arnold (10)
St Jude's CE Primary School, Portsmouth

Kenning Mermaid

Sea swimmer
Fin kicker.

Scale dresser
Hair comber.

Sweet singer
Shell collector.

Farideh Hashemi (10)
St Jude's CE Primary School, Portsmouth

Sweets

I dreamt I found
A sweetie village
On the northern coast.
Liquorice dogs,
Marshmallow cats,
Candy kids,
Sour adults,
Jelly babies
And sugar bees.
Fairies come as cakes,
Gingerbread houses
And cookie pavements,
Fizzy pop rivers
And lollipop chimneys.
No school all week,
Chocolate seats
And burnt dough door mats,
Mint coats
And icing trees . . .
But then I awoke
And it was only
A dream!

Molly Turner & Madeleine Sandells (10)
St Jude's CE Primary School, Portsmouth

Teachers

In my memory bank
I remember when I was really young,
That nightmare fear
When teachers ruled the world.
That's the time we all regret
When I was really young.

Georgina Cullen (10)
St Jude's CE Primary School, Portsmouth

The Thing Under My Bed

Creeping, crawling
Every night,
Under my bed
I'm in a fright.

Sliding, slithering,
Looking for food
Under my bed,
It's very rude.

Sneaking, peeking
Through my stuff,
Making a noise
That's very rough.

Squeaking, squealing,
Knocked for seven,
Under my bed
They're no longer,
Now in Heaven.

Anaas Elshwiahad (10)
St Jude's CE Primary School, Portsmouth

Tiger

A stripy fighter
A ferocious biter.

A rapid hunter
A high jumper.

A fast crawler
A loud roarer.

A quiet sleeper
A terrifying leaper.

Who am I?
A tiger.

Poppy Huntley (11)
St Jude's CE Primary School, Portsmouth

An Annoying Kenning

An annoying crier,
A brilliant liar.

A stuff taker,
A troublemaker.

A football player,
A good vase slayer.

A stupid thinker,
A trespassing slinker.

A lot of anger,
An evil head banger.

Who am I?
A brother of course!

Elissa Churchill (11)
St Jude's CE Primary School, Portsmouth

Dog Kenning

A cat chaser
A hole digger.

A brave soldier
A burglar catcher.

A loud barker
A quiet sleeper.

A fast runner
A sky diver.

A small pouncer
A bone eater.

Christopher Young (10)
St Jude's CE Primary School, Portsmouth

Lizard

A colour blender
A strong defender.

A long hiker
A fast striker.

A quick starter
A speedy darter.

A tail dropper
A heart stopper.

A tongue flasher
A claw thrasher.

What am I?
A lizard.

Ross Parkins (11)
St Jude's CE Primary School, Portsmouth

Kitten!

A sneaky fighter
A cheeky biter.

A mean scratcher
A mouse catcher.

A jumpy leaper
A heavy sleeper.

An awful eater
A brilliant beater.

A fast runner
A fan of summer.

Evangeline Grace Kleinen (11)
St Jude's CE Primary School, Portsmouth

Pyramid

A great Egyptian pyramid flashes in the sun,
Sometimes they remind me of an oddly shaped cross bun.
When the people visit it the curses are revealed,
I really, really want to know how the doors are sealed.
Of the people who manage to find a way inside,
Nobody knows what happened to them, maybe they just died.
Now the pyramid age is dead,
The curses fall down on the sand instead.

Alex Gilchrist (10)
St Jude's CE Primary School, Portsmouth

A Mystery Muncher

A bouncy bopper
A long eared dotter.

A lettuce eater
Who jumps a metre.

A silent watcher
A salad muncher.

I am a . . . ?

Nicola Cook (10)
St Jude's CE Primary School, Portsmouth

Slithery Snake

Slithery, slimy snake
Swims sometimes in the lake,
Looks like a log,
Beware in the fog.
He leaps and attacks, so watch your back!
Slithery, slimy snake.
Sssssssssssssss!

Nathan Matthews (11)
St Jude's CE Primary School, Portsmouth

Gran Poem

My gran is as silly as a clown,
Her hair is as white as a piece of paper,
Her eyes are as brown as a tree trunk,
Her face is yellow like a banana,
When she walks she is like a big, huge apple blowing up,
When she sits she is like a pretty princess,
But the best thing about my gran is she gives me
                           anything I like to have.

Jasmine Ray (9)
St Jude's CE Primary School, Portsmouth

My Gran

My gran is as cuddly as a bear,
Her hair is like silk,
Her eyes are like lights glowing,
Her face is like a paper bag.
When she walks she is like a kangaroo,
When she sits she is like a statue,
When she laughs, she is like a frog,
When she sleeps she is like a baby.
The best thing is she is mine.

George Leslie (9)
St Jude's CE Primary School, Portsmouth

Cat Kenning

Fur dresser
Fish eater

Bad swimmer
Terrible singer

Night prowler
Mouse catcher.

Victoria Burrows
St Jude's CE Primary School, Portsmouth

Elephant

Big ears,
huge plates on his head
flap like a bird's wings.

Enormous feet,
squashing machine,
trampling frightened insects into the ground.

Long trunk,
a hosepipe
squirting water on its humped back.

Long tusks,
giant spears
charge at tree trunks.

Large droppings
giant Easter eggs
that children don't want to eat.

Big puddles behind him
like orange juice
marking his territory.

Nina Pullen (11)
St Jude's CE Primary School, Portsmouth

My Gran

My gran is as happy as Mr Blobby,
Her hair is like white snow,
Her eyes are like sparkling crystals,
Her face is like a soft cat.
When she walks she is like a cat,
When she sits she is like a panther,
When she laughs she is like a leopard,
When she sleeps she is like a snail,
The best thing about my gran is no matter what she does, I love her.

Victoria Mills (9)
St Jude's CE Primary School, Portsmouth

My Gran

My gran is as gentle as a kitten,
Her hair is like a plate of spaghetti,
Her eyes are like glass marbles, always shining happily,
Her face is like a rotten apple,
When she walks, she is like a cat sprawling,
When she sits, she is like a hunched bear,
When she laughs she is like a child, giggling,
When she sleeps, she is like a log, never still,
The best thing about my gran is
She is excellent at making meringues.

Hannah Dawson (8)
St Jude's CE Primary School, Portsmouth

There Was A Little Girl Called Rose

There was a little girl called Rose,
Who loved using the hose.
She got into trouble
And burst like a bubble,
That stubborn little girl called Rose.

Zsuzsa Holmes (10)
St Jude's CE Primary School, Portsmouth

My Grandma

My gran is a cool and groovy chick,
Her hair is as wild as a grey bunny rabbit,
Her eyes are like a baboon's face,
Her face looks like some thin whiskers are striped across her face,
When she walks, she is like a chair with her bottom sticking out.
When she sits, she is like a wriggly little worm.
When she laughs she is like a hyena sniggering,
When she sleeps she is like a neighing horse.
The best thing about my gran is that she is wonderful.

Charlotte Race (8)
St Jude's CE Primary School, Portsmouth

Sweets

Sweets, yummy sweets,
They are all tasty treats.

You could have some lemon drops
Or some jelly tots.

Suck it,
Chew it,
Crunch it,
Munch it.

Sweets, yummy sweets,
They are all tasty treats.

Amie Gissing (10)
St Jude's CE Primary School, Portsmouth

Snow

S lippery, slushy snowballs,
N o land can be seen that isn't like a white wonderland,
O h, I love the sparkling quilt shimmering on the ground,
W e all adore having fun in the snow.

Charlotte Warren (8)
St Jude's CE Primary School, Portsmouth

Snow

S lushy, slippery snow,
N orth is covered, tip to toe,
O h hooray we get to go
W ith all friends to drink hot cocoa.

Hannah Bettey (8)
St Jude's CE Primary School, Portsmouth

Snow

Snow is very bold,
even when it's cold.

Snow is rather sloppy,
it freezes all the poppies.

Snow is glistening
when I'm listening.

Snow is falling gently
even on Mr Bentley.

Snow is wonderful
and very fundable.

Snow is white
and very bright.

Snow is pretty
and very witty.

Snow is ploughed out of the drive
then I see a beehive!
Snow is on the window ledge
and even on the top of the hedge.

Now it is time,
the icicles chime.

On the Christmas tree there is fake snow,
then Father Christmas says, 'Ho, ho!'

Kizzy Laundon (8)
St Jude's CE Primary School, Portsmouth

Snow

S ilvery, sparkling snow
N o more sun for a while,
O n the frosty bench in the house,
W ater frozen in the street.

Zac Holloway (8)
St Jude's CE Primary School, Portsmouth

Spring

S pring is as bright as a Hawaiian shirt,
P ink flowers are all in bloom,
R oses are red, violets are blue,
I n the river fish are swimming,
N ettles are stinging everyone,
G rass is as green as seaweed.

Sophie Mason (9)
St Jude's CE Primary School, Portsmouth

Snow

S lushy, sparkling, soft snow,
N uts are hidden under glistening snow,
O ver the white mountains the children play,
W eather is freezing and I am wrapped up warm,
   Snuggly and comfortable am I.

Hannah Duffy (8)
St Jude's CE Primary School, Portsmouth

Snow

S now is cold and slushy,
N obody dislikes it,
O h how snow is so wonderful,
W e all love snow.

Lauren Butler-Todd (8)
St Jude's CE Primary School, Portsmouth

My Gran

My gran is as brainy as a computer.
My gran's hair is as grey as a hippo.
My gran's eyes are as blue as a swimming pool.
My gran's face is as wrinkly as a bulldog's face.
When she walks she hobbles like a penguin.
When she sits she's like a sat up skull.
When she laughs she's out of control.
When she sleeps it's like she's dead.
But the best thing about my gran is she spoils me.

Charlotte Cameron (8)
St Jude's CE Primary School, Portsmouth

Snow

S now angels are on the ground.
N umb fingers are frozen with ice.
O h! So slushy and slippery.
W hite snow is floating gracefully.

Kiera Saville (8)
St Jude's CE Primary School, Portsmouth

Snow

S ilvery white wonderful stuff,
N ow tumbling from the clouds above.
O f all the world's brilliant gifts
W e all love snow.

Theo Read (8)
St Jude's CE Primary School, Portsmouth

Life

As the well dressed nurse gives you a gift,
It's a small baby, he moves his eyelid.
You see a sparkle in the eye of the child,
Touch his bald head so tender and mild.

As you take him outside, he learns to walk.
As you sing him songs, he learns how to talk.
He learns to misbehave, imitate and annoy.
He starts getting a caring for a small plastic toy.

He has just finished his first school year,
He's then down the pub with his mates drinking beer.
He's now got a girlfriend, then wife and now kid.
His brother is sick and his father dead.

He now has just realised he has wasted his life,
No longer has family, friends, kid or a wife.
He wishes he saw the world when he was young,
Too old now, too lazy and numb.

He looks at the sky way, way up there,
Rocking his last rock on his rocking chair.

This could be his last ever nap,
Knowing he might never come back.
He walks through a tunnel and heads for a gate,
And in a small room St Peter awaits.

He puts in the lock shiny gold keys,
You are left in a world of flowers and trees.
All you can do is admire and stare
At all the strange wonders you have come upon there.

When you see this you will start to believe,
There's more to life than to eat, drink and breathe.

Joseph Peace (11)
St Peter's School, Farnborough

The Solar System - Haiku

Jupiter is big,
The biggest planet by far,
Pluto is tiny.

Brendan Reis (9)
St Swithun Wells School, Eastleigh

Valentine's Day - Haiku

On Valentine's Day
Giving beautiful roses
As a sign of love.

Millie Hibberd (9)
St Swithun Wells School, Eastleigh

Space - Haiku

Saturn has a ring,
Pluto has not got a ring,
Earth has life on it.

Ben Dare (9)
St Swithun Wells School, Eastleigh

Roses - Haiku

Roses are pretty
And they are so colourful
And bright and lovely.

Kurtis Senter (8)
St Swithun Wells School, Eastleigh

On Valentine's Day - Haiku

On Valentine's Day,
I come here today to say,
Sweet love is true love.

Sophia Winter (9)
St Swithun Wells School, Eastleigh

Red Valentine - Haiku

Red is there for love,
Red is a symbol of love,
Red is for love now.

Danielle Coombs (8)
St Swithun Wells School, Eastleigh

Nature - Haiku

Nature's calm like leaves,
Nature's calm like red berries,
Nature's calm like grass.

Laura Moore (8)
St Swithun Wells School, Eastleigh

Flowers - Haiku

Flowers are smelly,
Bushes and trees are pretty,
Doggies are lovely.

Rebecca Man (8)
St Swithun Wells School, Eastleigh

In London

In London I heard people shouting,
people running, people screaming.
In London I saw crowds of people,
people pushing, surrounded by tall buildings
and the stretching sea.
In London I thought I was lost,
I thought I was alone.
In London I said I was scared,
I said I was alone.

Hannah Preston (10)
St Swithun Wells School, Eastleigh

Swimming Lessons

In the lesson I heard shouting and laughing,
In the lesson I thought I wouldn't do well,
In the lesson I said nothing, I was speechless,
In the lesson I saw the teacher and the other children,
In the lesson, in the end, I learned how to swim.

Mark Hubbard (11)
St Swithun Wells School, Eastleigh

On The Boat

On the boat I saw people watching TV and people eating,
On the boat I heard people talking and shouting,
On the boat I thought about sinking and dying,
On the boat I said, 'How come the boat's shaking so violently?'

Emily Lewis-Brown (11)
St Swithun Wells School, Eastleigh

At The Football Match

At the football match
I said, 'I'm nervous.'

At the football match,
I saw the green pitch.

At the football match,
I saw the TV cameras.

At the football match
I thought, *am I going to mess up?*

At the football match
I thought, *what do I do?*

At the football match,
I heard the crowd,

At the football match,
I heard the players
Muttering to themselves.

Chris Greep (10)
St Swithun Wells School, Eastleigh

The Rainbow

The rainbow is like coloured cobwebs,
Hanging on the light,
With its sparkling crystals tied on,
Gleaming ever so bright.

People say at the end of the rainbow
A gift is in store,
A pot of gold with a leprechaun on top,
Singing, 'Take more, take more.'

This coloured fantasy
Comes at a certain time,
It comes when the rain has gone
And the sun is ready to shine.

Kelly Johnston (10)
Sharps Copse Primary & Nursery School

I Dare You

Dear Mrs O'B

I dare you, double dare you, to stick your head
in the mouth of a tiger and tickle its tonsils with a sneeze.

Run across an alligator's back when it's just had its
teeth cleaned and sharpened by me!

Sit backwards on a charging rhino,
while drinking a boiling cup of tea.

To suck the poison out of an angry baboon's bum
when it's just been bitten by a snake - *see!*

To pluck the eyebrows of a tarantula
with your grandmother's false teeth.

I dare you, *double dare you,* to visit my world, my zoo!
If you don't I may just come to visit you!

PS Oh, and with most of my zoo . . .

Christopher King (10)
Sharps Copse Primary & Nursery School

A Rap

I went to a dance on a red, red night,
There was hot, hot music at the hall tonight;
We danced all night in the lights so bright,
Hip, hip, hop for the dance tonight.

Jasmine Crickmay (10)
Sharps Copse Primary & Nursery School

Boots

Who's wearing the wellington boots?
A farmer who's slopping and slushing in mud,
Tired and weary, milking his cows,
That's who's wearing the wellington boots.

Liah Robbins (11)
Sharps Copse Primary & Nursery School

Schooldinnerwocky

(Based on 'Jabberwocky' by Lewis Carroll)

'Twas Monday and the dinner ladies
Did gire and gimble in the hall.
All mimsy was Miss Slaughterpork
And Miss Mince wanted to kill all.

Beware the Schooldinnerwocky my friend!
Her potatoes that hurl, her gravy that splashes!
Beware the head knife and fork, and shun
The lettuce that comes out in rashes!

She took her pizza spatula in hand:
Long time the problem's end she sought -
So she rested, she slew the soft toffee
And sat awhile in thought.

And as in toughish thought she sat,
The Schooldinnerwocky with eyes of Marmite,
Came carrotting through the cafeteria doors,
His biscuit hands put up for a fight.

She thought very quickly as he passed slickly
The well placed milk went splisher-splash.
She left him surprised and with the pies
Back she sped in a flash.

'And hast thou got the pies, Tracy?
Come to our table,' beamed a dinner lady.
'Oh fantastic day, quelle heure Calais,'
They sang in their praise.

'Twas Monday and the dinner ladies
Did gire and gimble in the hall.
All mimsy was Miss Slaughterpork
And Miss Mince wanted to kill all.

Efe Gere (11)
Sharps Copse Primary & Nursery School

Personification

The wind howled at the sky,
The car swallowed hard as it ran,
The street light shone on the pavement,
The fence picked its splinters off,
The grass bled when it was cut,
The thunder shouted at me.

Damien Wren (10)
Sharps Copse Primary & Nursery School

Boots And Shoes

Who's wearing the football boots?
Beckham, the greatest free kicker,
With the ball like a speeding bullet
Faster than the eye can see;
That's who's wearing the football boots.

Louis Landers (10)
Sharps Copse Primary & Nursery School

Noisily

Noisily the tiny dog barked at the neighbours,
Noisily the music echoed through the walls,
Noisily the knife scraped as it sharpened,
Noisily the train rattled past in the distance,
Noisily my baby cousin screamed in anger,
Noisily the balloon went *pop!*

Lauren Galmoye (10)
Sharps Copse Primary & Nursery School

Carpet

Dear Mrs Davis

I am your classroom carpet,
I am fed up with your class,
Sometimes they run on me,
Sometimes they sit on me,
Sometimes they stamp on me
And they really, really hurt me.
They talk all the time
And that does your head in
You're the worst.
When you shout, it is really, really loud.
You pop my eardrums.
Could you please calm down?

Yours sincerely
Fluffy Cotton

Kevin Draycott (11)
Sharps Copse Primary & Nursery School

Shoes

Who's wearing the ballet shoes?
Sara, the ballerina, on her tiptoes,
Getting ready for a twirling, whirling performance,
With a leap and a high leg spin, applause and a cheer,
She has won the gold medal because she's the best!
That's who's wearing the ballet shoes.

Dawn Creamer (10)
Sharps Copse Primary & Nursery School

The Seasons

Autumn is a rainbow,
Autumn is my wardrobe,
Autumn is a treasure chest,
Autumn looks lovely.

Winter is a wonderland,
Winter is my dream,
Winter is beautiful.

Spring smells gorgeous,
Spring is sweet,
Spring is warm,
Spring is a bunch of flowers.

Summer is a desert,
Summer is an oven,
Summer is a hot bath,
Summer is great fun.

Karley Chandler (10)
Sharps Copse Primary & Nursery School

Personification

The clouds poured with rain,
The car spat out its petrol,
The grass tickled my feet,
The banana blushed when its skin was pulled down,
The apple wailed when bitten
And the numbers in maths muddled themselves up.

Nicole Horn (10)
Sharps Copse Primary & Nursery School

Animals

Under the ocean, under the sea,
Down by the seaweed, where you can see
A magical selection of fishes and eels
And all the other animals with fins and gills.
You can dance with the dolphins
And swim with the sharks,
Under the ocean, under the sea.
In the Australian outback, the Aussie bush,
By the midsummer's light, the winter's ambush,
There is a wide variety of things to catch your eye,
And here are some of the animals that you might spy:
Kangaroos bouncing or koalas bathing,
Or maybe even a snake,
But if you see a King Brown, run for goodness sake!
In the Australian outback, the Aussie bush.

Emma Morgan (11)
Sherborne House School

Feelings

Sorrow is dark and cold,
Love is emotional and strong,
Happiness is warm and friendly,
Anger is hard and heartless,
Loneliness is miserable and friendless,
Feelings are alive and trapped,
Let them out!

Jenny Hadnutt (10)
Sherborne House School

Seasons On A Wheel

Icy was the mountain,
The wind as cold as steel,
Frozen was the fountain,
Frost-covered, the field.

As time passed, the waters
Started again to flow,
And older rabbits' daughters
Were born and started to grow.

In summer, lovely ice creams
Were sold once again,
And people had icy dreams
Inside a shady den.

When autumn came,
And leaves started to fall,
We thought it would never be the same,
But the wheel brings it round again . . . again . . . again . . .

Rebecca Thomas (11)
Sherborne House School

The Waves Of Time

The waves of the ocean rule the sea,
People always think they know the timing of arrival,
Until they're proven wrong.
After a while, their worries are gone,
And so are their lives,
For they have been claimed by the waves of time.

Tom Metcalf (10)
Sherborne House School

Dragons

The funny thing about dragons is
They're completely unpredictable,
One minute they're calm and peaceful
Then they scorch your kitchen table.

Don't fall for the puppy dog eyes
Or the gentle wagging tail,
Because once you let it in your house
Who knows, it could read your private mail.

So if you see one coming up the drive
Just take a broomstick and yell, *'Scat!'*
Wave a hosepipe around in the air
To make sure they don't come back.

Matthew Crouch (10)
Sherborne House School

The Maze

I was lost in a maze,
All was a daze,
I was in there for hours,
Tired and thirsty.
I cried for help,
There was no reply.
Then through the darkness
I saw a flicker of light,
Anticipation of escape,
I ran to the last glimmer of sunlight,
Able to watch the golden sunset,
Freedom at last.

Andrew Harrington (11)
Sherborne House School

The Sea

In the icy depths of the Atlantic,
Below the pounding waves,
Many a creature makes its home,
Among the rocks and caves.
No prey nor predator can survive
If they don't keep a constant eye
On all their neighbours, big and small,
And even the fisherman's haul.
Whilst treacherous storms rage above,
Which cause a dangerous tide,
Deadly creatures lurk under rocks,
Where sea fish try to hide.
But as the storm begins to break,
And the waves begin to calm,
The ocean creatures start to emerge,
Which have caused sailors harm.
An eel and a jellyfish slip and slide,
Gliding out from crevices below.
An angler fish comes swimming by
With a strange and eerie glow.
All different kinds of animals
Then come sliding out
From tiny plankton to a huge blue whale
With water shooting out of its spout.
The lovely colours of the fish
Pink, blue, red and green,
All these wonderful colours,
The most I've ever seen.
So let's give thanks for the wonders of nature
And the beauty of the sea!

Joshua Peppiatt (10)
Sherborne House School

Under The Sea

There are many creatures under the sea,
The angelfish with all its colours,
And the great white shark with its snappy teeth.
The moray eel with its slithery body,
And the stingray with its deadly tail.
The puffer fish that swells like a balloon,
And the jellyfish, like a plastic bag.
The crab with its crunching claws,
And the octopus with its many legs.
It's a wonderful world under the sea,
With plenty to explore.

Thomas Bruss (11)
Sherborne House School

Autumn

Autumn's here,
Leaves are falling,
Gone for another year.
But when the sun hits those golden, crispy leaves lying on the ground,
All the months of winter coldness are worth it.
Animals are changing,
Crops are dying,
The sun has set
And the mood is right.

Alexa Thiel (11)
Sherborne House School

The Day I Got Stuck Up A Tree

The day I got stuck up a tree.
I saw the postman, Jeff,
I shouted but he didn't hear
And I remembered he was deaf.

The cat climbed up to join me
And licked me on my face,
We didn't know what to do,
We were both stuck in this place.

The milkman came to bring the milk
But dropped it on the mat,
He thought no one had noticed
But didn't see me or the cat.

Along came an old granny
With her skirt stuck in her knickers,
Oh I did feel sorry for her,
Poor old Mrs Snickers.

Along came some schoolgirls
Who called me a fool,
But I had the last laugh
Coz I wasn't going to school!

At last the firemen came,
I was feeling very cold,
I was mighty glad to see them
As I wasn't feeling so bold.

Jenny Patterson (10)
Sherborne House School

Good Play

Today we made a pirate ship
Right at the top of the stairs.
Sue was the captain, I was the mate
And the cabin was made out of chairs.

The kitchen was our first stop
But the boat ran aground.
We jumped off the ship and went on a search
And hobby horses were what we found.

We captured my mum who was by the sink,
She said she was Captain Hook.
She promised us treasure, a bun and a cake,
But we had just made her our cook.

We both rode back to our wonderful ship
But Sue fell and hurt her head.
I ran to the rescue but made a big mess,
So we both got sent straight to bed.

Katriina Gifford-Hull (11)
Sherborne House School

Squeaky Stair

There once was a squeaky old stair
Which led to Benjamin's lair.
It squeaked coming down,
Made you look like a clown,
So everyone knew you were there!

Benjamin Brown (10)
Sherborne House School

As I Walked Past

As I walked past,
I saw the sheep
On the hillside.
I saw the sun
Shining on the tide.
I saw the dew
Upon the grass,
As I walked past,
As I walked past.

As I walked past,
I saw the sea,
The gleaming sparkle.
I saw the sand,
The golden colour.
I saw the children
Playing with each other,
As I walked past,
As I walked past.

As I walked past,
I saw the moon,
Half with a face.
I saw the stars,
Sparkly stars.
I saw the sun setting,
It looked like Mars,
As I walked past,
As I walked past.

Ruby Jackson (10)
Sherborne House School

Spring Surprise

S pring brings flowers blooming,
P riceless yet rare.
R ich green grass flowing,
I n the calming air.
N ever a willow stops to rest instead,
G liding through the air.

S pring brings the baby animals,
U nique is each one.
R ough are some,
P olite but fun.
R abbits have their kittens,
I n meadows they hop in the sun.
S heep have their lambs,
E ver grazing, never done.

Stephanie Ellis (11)
Sherborne House School

The Children's Prayer

Let the teachers in our school
Not be strict or uncool,
Come to school all scruffy and meek,
And let the cooks make lots of meat.

Let the food be much more nice,
And the options beans and rice.
The school lunches are ever so sick,
Why can't we just take our pick?

When we're naughty the teachers go mad
Their blood boils like our dad's.
Let them, Lord, please give less work,
And especially of homework.

When they're preaching make us less bored,
Let them give the answers, Lord.

Nikhil Bassi (10)
Sherborne House School

Lazy Lily

Lazy Lily hates to work,
She finds picking up her pencil way too much,
She sits on her chair, staring into space,
And daydreams about the amazing fair.

Her teachers moan and groan,
Can't stop twittering about her in the staffroom,
'Why don't you tidy your room?' asks her mother.
'You must stop lazing around, Lily,' they all say.

Lazy Lily hates to work,
She finds picking up her pencil way too much,
Now she sits on the sofa watching TV,
Waiting to watch 'Tom and Jerry'.

Lynn Wambua (10)
Sherborne House School

Daydream

I am a little tired,
I want to go to sleep,
I want to go back home,
Into my bed I'll creep.

I am a little bored,
I don't know what to do,
Should I think for once,
Or maybe play a chord or two?

Lucy Higgins (10)
Sherborne House School

Spring

Spring is here,
There is blossom on the trees,
Children are playing happily
With each other,
Chicks are waiting to be fed,
Cows are munching
On the long, lush, green grass.
Ponies are galloping
Around the field
Chasing each other.
Puppies are suckling
On their mother's milk.
Spring has come once again.

Catherine Clay (11)
Sherborne House School

Why Must I . . . ?

I've got to write a poem,
I don't know what to say.
I've paced the room and sat and tried
In every single way.
Monday is the deadline,
Tuesday's far too late.
The trouble is to find some words
That poetically relate.
My mum and dad are driven mad,
And I am quite insane,
Because I have to write this poem.
My teacher is to blame!

Paulus Randall (10)
Sherborne House School

My Dog

He doesn't even woof a please,
To get a slice of smelly cheese,
He takes old tea bags out the bin,
And licks old bottles of medicine.
If Mum won't buy him some food, perhaps,
He'll whine and bark and (on purpose) collapse.
If you forget to put his food out,
He'll pull a face and give you a pout.
Apricots, apple cores, oranges, plums,
Lamb chops, chicken and even ox tongue!
There isn't a thing that this dog won't eat,
He'll even lick dirty, smelly feet!

He sleeps in a basket under the stairs,
Along with all the broken chairs,
He snuggles down and has a sleep,
And when he does we have a peep.
He plays with all his squeaky toys,
And chases all the naughty boys!
He barks at all the neighbours' cats,
And scares off all the smelly rats.
We take him for lots of beautiful walks,
And sometimes I pretend that he talks.

Kirsten Adamson (10)
Sherborne House School

The Battle

The axe fell,
The sword sang,
And in the hills, the horns rang.
Cavalry spoiled the ground with their heavy hooves,
But even then, surely we would lose.
It was then the Dark Lord fell,
But the slayer, his life did proudly sell.
Then the army of darkness died, powerless,
And light shone. Bright and shadowless.

Matthew Culmer (10)
Sherborne House School

Safari

Your tent is just like a greengrocer's,
Comforting, you may think!
You can smell all those delicious fruits,
Which ones shall you choose?

The giraffes, they do like their baths,
So does everyone, I suppose.
They eat all day and sleep all night,
Just like humans do.

The hyenas, they're a savage lot,
Just like our bullies and burglars.
Steal from anyone, to give to themselves,
But that is what they're supposed to do.

The African plain is a circle of life,
Each animal has its own lifestyle.

Sophie Crafter (10)
Sherborne House School

Listen, Listen To The Night

Listen, listen to the night,
All you hear is silent life.
Ghosts wandering here and there,
Witches whispering, so beware,
Vampires sucking blood from dead bodies,
Giants blowing dreams in troubled ears,
For a silent night with nothing to fear.
Listen, listen to the night,
All you'll hear is silent life.

Hollie Smith (11)
Sherborne House School

The Very Important Meeting

People of the school
Listen to me please, I have some important information
That will affect the entire nation!
We have a massive meeting
And an amazing two chairs for seating!
This is due to a fierce bear,
Which has just escaped from the fair!
This has nothing to do with school,
It only bashed down our hall!
Remember there's lots of seating, so please come,
It will be strict and serious and we shall have some fun!

Car park is available, but no cars allowed,
You must whisper, you do this out loud!
The only things allowed are small, light snacks,
For this I recommend a large portion of lamb racks!
If you are polite you will be caught in a net,
Please be rude and you will be rewarded, you bet!
The meeting will start at nine like a harp,
So please arrive at eleven o'clock sharp!

Who would like to be at this meeting?
Don't forget the seating.
Why is everyone running through the door?
For some reason they are retreating!

Adam Moussa (10)
Sherborne House School

Dreaming

Past the mountain
With a snow-capped peak,
Past the mountain
Above the clouds,
Past the mountain's
Rock-covered face,
Across the sandy plain
To the blackened creek.
I lie there,
Quiet and dreaming.
I never want to wake up.
I want to stay fast asleep.
I'll be dreaming for all of my life,
From now on,
Forever.

Aaron Piper (10)
Sherborne House School

The Horses

The horses in the field next to us,
Come up and wait for vegetables.
They're always there for me, except in winter,
When they're in the stables getting fed by the vicar.
When I see them I only see four,
But the big chestnut can be a bore.
When I feed them leaves,
The big chestnut heaves.
A small, brown, cheeky one is my favourite,
I wish he was mine.

Catherine Whalley (10)
Sherborne House School

Do You Listen To A Word I Say?

'Did you have a good day at school, poppet?'

'Well, you know what it's like,
I saw an elephant riding a bike.
Then someone pushed me in a cupboard, can you guess who?
It was that awful Mark, I flushed him down the loo!
At break I ran away to Scotland to do the Highland fling,
After several cuts and a few bruises, I decided it was not my thing.
I hijacked a jet to get back in time for lunch,
Unfortunately I landed with a sickening crunch.
I was stranded with a great big gorilla called Smee,
Who tried to eat me for his tea!
I called out loudly for help in fear,
I screamed and I yelped, but then I heard a cheer.
The Queen had come to my rescue with a band and a crowd,
She chucked me on a jet and said, 'We are very proud.'
I landed in the playground with a bump and a jerk . . .'

'That's lovely, poppet, now get on with your homework!'

Sophie Bowyer (11)
Sherborne House School

Cats

Cats are adorable creatures,
Cats have strange features,
Cats have long, pointy ears,
Cats have many fears.

Cats are small but chunky,
Cats, well, mine's a bit funky,
Cats are normally small,
Cats, some are quite tall.

Cats are very bouncy,
Cats can be quite fancy,
Cats grow older by the second,
Cats, up to Heaven they are beckoned.

Gemma Crouch (11)
Sherborne House School

My Mum

Caring but competitive,
very, very supportive,
works like a horse all day long,
always doing exciting things,
likes to read, likes to walk,
often in for a long, girlie talk.

Sometimes fun,
often doubting herself,
she teaches a lot of chemistry,
likes to sit back - listen to music,
occasionally sarcastic.
She does a lot for the family,
though is firm when she needs to be.
That's my mum all of these things,
she's perfect, just for me.

Sophie Tait (9)
Sherborne House School

Monster

Monster, monster, hiding under the bed,
Monster, monster, banged me on the head,
Monster, monster, running down the stairs,
Monster, monster, eating all the chairs,
Monster, monster, sitting on my mattress,
Monster, monster, munching on an atlas,
Monster, monster, lying on the floor,
Monster, monster, is he breathing anymore?
Monster, monster, I called 999,
Monster, monster, nobody on the line!
Monster, monster, I shook his head,
Monster, monster, he is dead!

Dennis Glover (9)
Sherborne House School

Bubblegum

Bubblegum is my favourite sweet,
When I go to the candy shop
It's my special treat.

Blowing bubbles that reach out to space,
Oh no!
It has burst all over my face.

My favourite flavours are strawberry and cherry,
Lemon, apple, orange and berry.

I can chew and chew and chew all day,
All through school, even lunch and play!

When I get home I run to the drawer,
Because I know I can get some more.

Bubblegum is soft and deliciously chewy,
But I like it the best when it's sticky and gooey.

Olivia Snow (10)
Sherborne House School

Mummy! Mummy!

Mummy, Mummy, take me home,
Mummy, Mummy, answer the phone,
Mummy, Mummy, have you heard?
Mummy, Mummy, that's absurd.
Mummy, Mummy, here's a book,
So Mummy, Mummy, cook, cook, cook,
Oh, Mummy, Mummy, I'm losing my voice.
(That'll stop the noise!)

Oliver Dempster (10)
Sherborne House School

There Is In Me . . .

There is in me . . .
    A robin,
    Chirpy, cheerful and cheeky,
    Always on the lookout
    For a tit-bit.
    Running here and there,
    Bright clothes,
    Attracting attention.

There is in me . . .
    A tiger,
    Wise but sometimes wild.
    Fast, so much so
    That when you blink
    You've missed me.
    We love to hide in long grass,
    But watch for our stripes.

There is in me . . .
    A kid goat
    Not liking to be tied up.
    Tethered to one spot
    Nibbling nothing.
    Fierce at times
    Especially when
    I kick in rugby.

There is in me . . .
    A snow leopard
    Who adores to climb
    Gracefully and noislessly
    In our favourite habitat.
    We brush our cheeks
    Against our furry shoulder blades,
    Feeling dreamily comfortable.

There is in me . . .
A mole
Who sometimes cannot see
What everyone else can.
Rough velvet.
I love digging in the garden
But my mum isn't pleased
Because of the mess.

Freya Jones (10)
Sherborne House School

Red

Red is the colour of warning,
It's bright red flashing lights,
It's a sign of danger,
It's foxes prowling at night.

It's hot volcano lava,
It's cruel vampire eyes,
It's dripping blood from a vicious wound,
It's swollen spots and sties.

Red is a beautiful sunset,
It's apples, all rosy and red,
It's a shiny, ruby necklace,
It's poppies in a flower bed.

It's cherries in a basket,
It's roses in a posy,
It's a heart in a Valentine's card,
It's cheeks all red and rosy.

Hollie Cooper (10)
Sherborne House School

Smile

Sadness lives in the darkness,
It comes out when you are lonely,
It hits you when you're on your own.
If you're not happy it creeps up on you,
And can make you feel all glum.
It can spread into other people,
And make your friends feel bad.
It will try to come after you,
But wait, there is a way to stop it.
It's a brilliant, fabulous way!
You have to be brave to do it,
It's not really a secret,
So I shall share it with you.
It's very simple,
The answer is to *smile!*

Charlie Clay (9)
Sherborne House School

Ruth

Ruth has silky long hair
That is always tied back
Wide blue eyes
And powerful eyebrows
She is always truthful
A faithful friend
She has a big delightful smile
She also eats a lot
She is very tall
But she tries to fit in
She loves animals
And also apples!
She is a bit mad
But we always get along,
We are very good mates, Ruth and me.

Hannah Clarke (10)
Sherborne House School

My Brother

My brother, Christopher, is my best friend.
He is rather witty, silly and sometimes sly.
Reading is his favourite hobby,
I am sure to find him clutching a book,
A true sign of a bookworm.
Rather good at swimming, he loves doing the front crawl.
He is bright in English and the most excellent story writer.
With black hair, he can easily be seen in crowds.
Sport is not his favourite subject,
But he still enjoys joining any game.
I love to play with him,
Even though he is annoying and irritating.
I would never ever sell him for he is the best brother ever.

Timothy McPhie (9)
Sherborne House School

Snowman

I made a little snowman,
Upon the kitchen floor,
I thought I'd keep it as a pet,
Till Rover came through the door.

Mom says he's not coming back,
Daddy says so too,
Brother says he doesn't care,
And sis says three is two!

The very next day it snowed again,
And I made another snowman,
I thought I'd keep it as a different pet,
Till the same Rover came through the door . . .

Ruth Yonge (10)
Sherborne House School

Is There A Goblin In My Cupboard?

It's dark and gloomy at night
Lights turned out, quiet as can be.
Noise in the cupboard, what can it be?
Cat, dog, guinea pig?
I wonder and wonder
Round goes my brain sister?
It cannot be, she is in bed,
Resting her sleepy head.
But what can it be, maybe a monster,
Maybe a mouse or a goblin?
Their evil eyes upon you, running through your head,
Scary as it can be.
All you want to shout is 'Mummy!'
Bulging fingers, like mouldy sausages touching your body.
Gnomes sniffing like sensors and then it all goes like a dream.
Mum's coming in,
'Mummy I had a nightmare!'

Kay Wheatley (9)
Sherborne House School

Blue Poem

Blue is the colour of the
Deep wide sea.
Blue is the colour of my
School diary.
Blue are my jeans
When I bounce on my trampoline.
Blue I feel when
My friends have been mean.
Naughty blue eyes of my
Brother at times.
Dark blue is my bedroom
Where I am typing this rhyme.

Tom Caldwell (9)
Sherborne House School

What Would I Do With No Food?

Food, food what would I do
If I didn't have you?
I'd be very sad
But also quite mad,
I'd chew the chairs
And maybe the stairs.

Feeling so hungry,
Gurgle, gurgle
My tummy would rumble.

I'd dream I would be at home,
Oh so humble,
I would lie on the grass
Eating ice cream
In a bowl made of glass.

Feeling so hungry
Gurgle, gurgle
My tummy would tumble.

Roast beef, lamb, chicken or veal
Every roast makes a delicious meal
Food, food what would I do
If I didn't have you?

Tristan Wong (9)
Sherborne House School

A New Member Of My Family, My Puppy

My puppy came from Portsmouth,
She's only ten weeks old,
She's gold and white, brown, black and blonde,
Everybody knows she loves to bond.

Nala is her name and she's quite tame,
She runs and hides all day long,
Then collapses on the floor,
All of a sudden,
She's up and gone.

Shih-Tzu is her breed,
How clever can they be!
She loves her food and puppy milk,
And always needs a bowl to be filled!

Anna Hannides (9)
Sherborne House School

Under The Ocean

Under the ocean, the white sharks swim,
Hunting fiercely before the light goes dim,
The little fish get caught in nets,
Whilst dolphins dance,
On the waves of white crests,
The sea hoses go through the ocean like darts
Whilst the whales sit and try to look smart,
The sea turtles swim very slow
And the flying fish jump up to your big toe,
The ocean is just such a wonderful place to be,
Now me and my mummy are going out to sea.

Natalie Cadde (10)
Sherborne House School

Cassia

I have a best friend
Her name is Cassia
She's loving and kind
Would never hurt a fly
She's glamorous
Has her ears pierced
Always wears trendy clothes
Gorgeous long brown hair
She's all hip and trendy
But not as good as gold
We throw popcorn at the cinema
Have a good time
She's brilliant at art
And an excellent singer
I suppose she chatters alot
Ever so friendly
Always there for me
Likes to read and loves sweets
Loves make-up, a great shopper
Has a cool dog
And a delightful family.

Kari Vigor (10)
Sherborne House School

Munching Menaces

My pets love eating books,
They had my dairy yesterday,
Now all my best loved secrets,
Are truly hidden away.

My pets love eating wood,
They'd scoff beds if they could,
Then we'd have to sleep on the floor,
And I can't stand wind under the door.

My pets love eating clocks,
By now they've eaten lots,
Now we have to stand in line,
Just so we can tell the time.

My pets love eating everything,
I'm going to tell you why,
My pets love eating everything,
Because my pets are crocodiles!

Anna Clark (9)
Sherborne House School

Tom G

My friend Tom is kind and helpful
And always tells the truth.
He's very funny
And had good manners.
Tom is likeable and doesn't swear,
I hope he stays my friend forever.
He likes his Game Boy, he plays it a lot
He has a bike and a scooter too,
A cool big brother and a little cat.
He's a trustworthy friend
And I hope he always will be.

Henry Fenton (9)
Sherborne House School

My Sweetest World

Just imagine a world made out of sweets,
You could take a nibble every five minutes!
The grass in the garden could be hundreds and thousands,
While the soil and mud could be chocolate cake.
Sugar mice would scuttle around the pebbled Smarties,
And marzipan flowers would blow in the breeze
Among the crush of sugared delights.

The houses are made of gingerbread and
The windows of thin ice sheets
And the pillars are made of rock,
The trees are filled with buttery dew,
With leaves that hang like shoe laces
With fruit pastels growing on them that drop off into the river,
Full of glassy icing that passes candy stick lamp posts,
And the branches, roots and stump of the trees
Are all made of tangled chocolate and fudge.

Sadly, children have eaten this world
So now it has vanished, the box all gone,
And I don't feel very well!

Harriet Lyons-Powell (9)
Sherborne House School

Humpty Dumpy

Humpty Dumpty sat on a wall,
Humpty Dumpty started to call,
'Get me down you filthy lot,
I'm stuck up here, I'm getting hot!'

The villagers below watched him sweat
And said 'Shall we get him down yet?''

'What! Get him down? That rotten old egg?
It's much more fun watching him beg.'

Annabel Brown (8)
Sherborne House School

The Ideal Person

Always on his Game Boy
Playing Pokémon
Trying to catch a Wurmple
Having tons of fun
When it comes to sports
Rugby is his game
He doesn't rate football
Even though most do
He is extremely strong
Through eating lots of food
He loves his Warhammer
His miniatures rule
He really hates Yu-gi-oh!
He says 'It should be shot!'
He has lots of freckles
With light brown hair
He is special because
He always tells the truth
He's reliable and funny
I can always count on him
He really is special.

Oliver Hoghton (9)
Sherborne House School

My Cat Lucky

My cat Lucky is a lucky cat
He always lives up to his name
He slept in a flowerpot once
Through the snow and rain
He found a warm place
In the tumble drier
But he didn't get tumbled!
He fell off my bunk bed
But didn't get hurt.
He toppled out of my window
But scrambled down to safety
He hid under the car
But didn't get run over
He escaped next-door's dog, - just.
If I tried any of that
I would be a mess
And I would never have survived
But Lucky is lucky.

Tom Grange (9)
Sherborne House School

Another Boring School Day

Brring, brring, school again,
Into class, forgot my pen.
Maths now, didn't revise,
Got a test, divide and times.
Out to break, icy cold,
Teacher comes, 'What have you been told?'
The only good lesson, English now,
Teacher comes in, you may sit down.
Horrid school dinners, at lunch break,
Mushy peas and rotten steak.
Science now, experiments galore,
The bell has gone, run for the door.

Jack Gavin (9)
Sherborne House School

Family

I always see grandad eating sweets
Or my sister sitting, waiting for treats,
Mother is always cleaning the house
And brother is always dissecting a mouse.

Father is always watching TV
Or calling up friends 'Please come to tea.'
Granny is so busy knitting
And baby is disgusting, always spitting.

Uncle Tim is always at the gym
And auntie is always crying,
My other uncle is a pilot
So he is always flying.

All my cousins' one, two and three,
Are boys who won't stop bullying me
And last of all there's little me
Who really does love her family!

Millie Heslam (9)
Sherborne House School

Snow

Everything is so beautiful,
Crisp white snow all around,
Glistening like icing sugar,
Nothing makes a sound.
Snow on leaves,
Glittering peacefully,
So delicate and white,
Even on my netball hoop.
It is such a magical sight.
Little snowflakes falling in the air,
Like fairies falling from the sky.
I think there really might be one -
My, oh my!

Anjelica Cleaver (8)
Sherborne House School

Mr Macker The Sweetie Shop Maker

Mr Macker makes shops
The shops that you don't normally see
They are made from anything
From gum to stretched toffee
I live in one of those shops
And you'll never guess what
We sell sweets that even your eyes won't believe
The little truffles are full of magic
The balls of gum are air
It will lift you off the ground before you can shout for anymore
The long marshmallows are scrumptious
The lovely strips of rock
The sweet that makes your teeth rot
There is all the chocolate you could hope for
As well as candy canes,
That comes in all colours
They're all so delicious
But I must go to serve my customers
What was that, sir?
The strip of rock that makes your teeth rot,
The long marshmallows, two balls of gum,
Oh and don't forget that candy cane.

Amy Cole (9)
Sherborne House School

There Is A Little Rebel

There is a little rebel who lives on top of my bed,
And when I won't wake up she'll jump right on my head.

There is a little rebel that when I get home from school,
My bedroom's suddenly a tip and she'll be having a ball.

There is a little rebel who no one thinks is true,
But when I'm going to a party, she'll take away my shoes.

There is a little rebel that when I'm going somewhere fun,
She will throw a little tantrum and say, 'I want to come.'

There is a little rebel who wears jeans and a little petal top,
Then when I do something naughty she'll threaten to call the cops.

There is a little rebel who's only as big as my finger,
But when there's sweets around, she always tends to linger.

There is a little rebel who's famous for her naughty game,
But when she plays it round me, guess who gets the blame.

Rosie Day (9)
Sherborne House School

School

School, school, school,
Why is there such thing as school?
The teacher's strict,
The meals make you sick!
School, school, school,
Why is there such thing as school?
My friends are nice,
They give me advice,
Why is there such thing as school?
Let me think,
Oh, I know, school is cool!

Emma Hurley (9)
Sherborne House School

My Fantasy Friend

I have lots of friends,
But they seem too real.
I like the friend, I've had
Since I was three.
Sometimes she's an animal,
Or the one to tell me what to do.
Maybe my dream person,
The one I want to meet,
Every day she's different,
Depending on the mood I'm in,
She likes the things I like,
Or hates the things I hate.
She is always there,
To comfort in one way
Or another.
She helps me with tests,
Or when I have a problem,
Have you got a friend,
A special friend like mine?

Kirsty Lam (9)
Sherborne House School

My Dog

Her mouth is pink
Her fur's black as ink
She loves her walk
She can almost talk
She likes to sleep
And chase sheep
She goes for a run
And has lots of fun
She makes a mess
That's my dog Bess.

Sam Harper (8)
Sherborne House School

There Is In Me . . .

There is in me a bird
Singing while flying tree around tree,
Always busy.

There is in me a donkey,
Helpful, lonely most of the time,
Sad, invisible in some lessons.

There is in me a cat,
Lazy, cute,
Peaceful when I am ill,
But sharp, short nails.

There is in me a monkey,
Jumpy, cheeky,
Sneaky at home.

There is in me a giraffe,
Eating lots, drinking water,
Lots of friends to chat to.

There is in me a dog,
Shouting, loud, bouncy,
Mystifying, sniffing lots.

There is in me a lion,
Loving to play,
Looking for young,
Eating with my friends,
Wanting to be taken away by my mum.

Sophie Hawkes (9)
Sherborne House School

My Mummy

Always on the go
Working hard at the gym
Playing badminton
Stitching and doing embroidery
She bakes cakes and cookies
Specially for us
Cooking, mouth-watering
Indian food
But best of all
Her rice pudding
All yummy and scrummy
Drinking lots of tea
A pretty face
A warm smile
Perfect for a mum
Especially her cuddles
Even her kisses
Wearing dazzling Indian clothes
She doesn't wear high heels
But she loves jewellery
Beading charming bracelets
Especially for me
At bedtime saying
Sweet dreams
Ice creams
Lollipops
Smarties
After she's said goodnight
She collapses on the sofa and watches TV!

Gurleen Dhillon (10)
Sherborne House School

Mermaids

I can see mermaids swishing round a rock,
One with glittery blonde hair, another with jet-black,
Singing calm songs that make you go to sleep,
Playing with a beach ball smiling happily!
They ride on dolphins having fun adventures,
Then a shark scares them away.

Slippery pink coral tickles their feet,
Sea horses and starfish look beautiful and sweet!
Swirling and swimming away and away,
Talking to fish as they pass their day,
Mermaids play in their gardens under the sea,
Swirling through the waves, happy to be free.

Sparkly pearls in golden shells,
Lie nestling on the silvery sea floor,
The mermaids are sleeping silently now,
Resting on their rocks.

Reem Katifi (8)
Sherborne House School

Summer

S ummer is coming after all this time,
U nicorns come out to play,
M y mum makes lots of pies,
M y brother plays on my swing,
E veryone is having fun,
R obins sing in the trees.

Fiona McAllister (8)
Sherborne House School

The Funky Chicken

My name is Joe
And I'd like you to know
That I'm a DJ,
Who plays down at 'The Hay'

I spin those discs,
From morning to night
And it doesn't half give
The others a fright.

I play many gigs
For horses and pigs
And I'm doing one now
For Sunny the cow.

Right down in the barn,
All over the farm
No one's a missin'
The funky chicken.

Oliver Golden (8)
Sherborne House School

Colour

Black is night, stiller than coal,
White is whiter than your soul,
Red is deeper than ruby or blood,
Brown is the colour of wood or mud,
Green is the grass, subtle and mellow,
A banana, a lemon, they're both yellow,
Pink is the colour of ballet shoes
Or a sweet scented rose . . .
And purple for the heather in which you doze,
Blue is the sky in which the clouds roll by,
Orange is fire and the heart of a liar,
Silver is the colour of fairies' wings,
And gold is whatever each new day brings.

Isabella Letty (10)
Sherborne House School

Things I Like About Home

Bouncing on the beds,
Even though me mam says no,
Fighting with the cushions,
I just can't resist a little go.

Netball in the garden,
PlayStation inside,
Going on the climbing frame,
Finding places to hide.

Running, being noisy,
Across the wooden floor,
Sitting by the fire,
Hearing logs crackle and roar.

Listening to music,
Reading books galore,
I love my house, my home,
There's no place I love more.

Grace Long (9)
Sherborne House School

Questions?

Some people think a dream
Is the spirit inside us playing
Why don't we know
Why time is so short
And maths tests are so long?
How can we know
What Heaven looks like?
It might be all our favourite things,
What does a fairy's sneeze sound like
And where does a rainbow end?
Will learning ever come to an end?
I don't know any of these answers,
But I'll find them out one day!

Grace Dawes (10)
Sherborne House School

Friends

Everyone must have a friend
Otherwise sadness would never end.
A friend is generous and always kind,
And helps to take things off your mind.
Though you might fall out over something silly
You'll come back friends very quickly.
You might have some sort of secret club
Or play hide-and-seek behind the tubs.
Together you might have sleepovers, one, two and three,
Or go down to the beach and play in the sea.
If you're lucky, you'll go on holiday together,
And play in the pool, whatever the weather.

At school we mostly chat about my pet cat,
We get told off but we don't care,
We do each other's hair!
We get the same food at lunch
And together we munch.
At play we always say,
Hip, hip hooray!
We share our fun times
And never do bad crimes.
In the summer we pick flowers
And watch Austin Powers!
We play lots of games,
Like Guess who? And Monopoly too.
Our favourite food is pizza with garlic bread,
We do everything together,
That's what we've always said!

Holly Osmond-Smith (9)
Sherborne House School

Food I Like

I like . . .
Rice and beans
Pasta and bread
Potato and chips
Cornflakes after bed.

Vegetables and fruit
Yoghurt and biscuits
Sweets and chocolate too
Which aren't good for me.

Fizzy drinks and water
Milk and fruit juices
Soup with bread and
Crisps, chips and crackers.

Big fudge chocolate cakes
Along with pasties bakes
Sandwiches with cheese and cucumber
Or a bit of raspberry jam and butter.

Food oh food, lovely food
I just love it so much
Each day and each night,
Food oh food, whether it is good or it is bad
It will still be quite grand.

Lovely food, please never go away,
If I try something new,
I would still prefer my pasties bake.

Food oh food, just lovely food
Food oh food, what a lovely treat.

Sophie Moussa (8)
Sherborne House School

The Answer

Where is the answer book?
Is it in a desk
Or is it in the staffroom?
It may be in a bag,
Or we might be allowed to ask.
We could stay in at break time,
Let's look in a drawer,
Friends, help me look, let's find a calculator.
Oh no, it's got no batteries,
Now it's time for lunch.
Let's take the shortcut,
Get beans and mash,
Maybe a chocolate or two.
Go to the tuck shop,
Get Snickers and Twix,
Let's go and play table tennis,
With a friend or two.
Let's go back to the tuck shop,
The answer might be there,
I still can't find the answer book
We'll come back tonight.
I may just have to give up
And never get it right.

Alexandra Pringle (8)
Sherborne House School

My Pets Are Lovely

My pets are lovely, I have four of them,
Phoebe, Kitty, Bella and Lucky,
Phoebe is my number one,
She thinks I am her mum.

Kitty is a fluff ball,
She always miaows and calls,
She loves my mum and
She sits on her tum.

Lucky is very naughty,
He is the fatest boy on Earth,
He always flops on his back,
In front of the fire on the mat.

Bella is a scaredy cat,
You never ever see her,
I'd take a look now,
Run, run, Bella, out the cat flap.

Sarah Elizabeth Bull (8)
Sherborne House School

Sister, Sister
(Written for my big sister, Lizzie)

S ister, sister you're really kind,
I love the way you read my mind,
S miles and cuddles we have each day,
T ickling, teasing in every way,
E verything I borrow, you don't mind,
R eally bad things you don't find!

S winging gently on the rope swing,
I t's so nice we start to sing,
S urfing together in the blue sea,
T rying to fix the castle for me,
E eating ice creams before they melt,
R eally want you to know how I felt.

Annie Shawcroft (9)
Sherborne House School

The Scary School Dinner

Ring the bell it is time for lunch,
Let's see what we have got to munch,
Chicken eyes and worms too,
That makes a lovely stew!

Eat it up, gulp it down,
Stir it around as it goes a dark brown,
Bits of hair, and earwax too,
Forms a nice sticky glue.

Put your tongue back in your mouth,
Because the food is heading south,
Finish off your main course first,
Hurry! Slugs and snails are for desserts.

Pack up your cup and your plate,
Run outside before it's too late,
It's the end of lunchtime now,
What is that really awful smell?

Alice Neilson (9)
Sherborne House School

School

1   School is very good fun
2   I love school more than anyone,
3   It is the coolest school in the world
4   Because I made it with no help from you.

5   At school every day
6   The sun is shining, it's not grey,
7   The school lunches are not bad,
8   Even though they make me sad.

9   School is fun, school is great,
10 School has everything you can make
11 It's mine, it's mine, it's not yours for evermore,
12 School, school is . . . fantastic!

Philippa Dempster (9)
Sherborne House School

Slime

My snake Slime,
Likes to climb.
He annoys my neighbours,
With his cheeky grin,
He climbs up their shin,
And when I call him,
He's never about,
What a cheeky snake!

He's green and red,
With a scaly head,
He is long and thin,
And sleeps in a bin.
I love him dearly,
He's very cuddly,
And extremely warm,
And above all he's mine.

When I took him to school,
My friends told me off,
'Naughty girl,' said Mr Hall.
Olivia wanted to hold him,
Emma wanted to stroke him,
I wanted to feed him,
Sam wanted to scream.

My snake Slime,
Is very strange,
But is also so cool,
I am proud of Slime,
And so glad he's mine.

Isabel Wealleans (8)
Sherborne House School

Silly Old Man

I once met a silly old man
Who thought it would be fun
To give up his job
And build a tower to the sun.

He started with some wood
Which he thought would be good
Then he got some bricks
And added some sticks.

But when he got quite high
He started to cry
It got very hot
For the sun shone a lot.

So he turned right around
And went back to the ground
Where he sat for a while
On the bricks in a pile.

I once met a silly old man
Who thought it would be fun
To give up his job
And build a tower to the sun!

Jack Culmer (8)
Sherborne House School

My Sister

My sister thinks she is the boss,
She really, really makes me cross,
She is eleven
In Year 7
And thinks nothing of me.

She picks on me,
Just like I'm a flea,
I'm her slave
If only she would live in a cave
See what the spiders think of her.

She is my sister
She looks like a blister
She's really old now,
I don't know how,
I wish she would disappear.

She has a head
Which is made of lead,
I would like to break her bones,
Or steal her mobile phone.
She makes me feel like I'm not here!

That's my sister!

Natalie Fairhurst (9)
Sherborne House School

Spook

When you're on the coast,
Look out for the ghost,
If you take a tiny peek
You might just grow a beak.

When the vampire's on his way,
Carry a Milky Way,
If you use a Mars bar,
It will sink into the tar.

Look out at night,
You're in for a fright,
When the skeletons are near,
Have a big cheer,
Or drink a bottle of beer.

When you get your hat
Look out for the bat,
They'll be spinning around your head,
Before you go to bed.

Sean Laidlaw (8)
Sherborne House School

The Beach

The beach is such a wonderful place to play,
Where lots of shells and sandcastles are made.
The beach is the place where I go in the summer,
When crabs are scuttling about in the sand.

The sea is packed with playing children,
All the fish scatter further out to sea,
Where fishermen are fishing,
At one o'clock all the children are
Having lunch on the beach.

At two o'clock all the children have
Finished their lunch and play on the sand,
Lazy days at the beach are fun,
Swimming and playing,
Until dusk has come.

Andrew Jones (8)
Sherborne House School

Hot Chill

Heat is in the desert made
Of the sand,
Terrifying scorpions all around me,
Cool fresh water from the deep well,
Hot people need a drink,
In the shade of leaning palm trees,
Little bugs scuttle about in the day,
Looking for shelter before the freezing night.

Samuel Grange (8)
Sherborne House School

Rugby!

We are the champions
We are the best
Scoring tries
And kicking the ball high!
Run fast and slow
It's all about go, go, go!
Steal the ball
Quick, come on let's go!
Tackle the Barbarians
Score like mad
It's too easy being bad!
Scrum and score,
Enter the war!
Penalty pass
Not near the grass
Aim high
For a try!
Jonny Wilkinson scored and won
For us to be number one!

Gabriella Oliver (9)
Sherborne House School

My Dog Arthur

My dog Arthur, he eats like a hog,
He'll eat carrots, chocolate and even broccoli!
And if you saw him in the kitchen then he'd
Be drinking black top tea!
My dog Arthur is so dopey, he wouldn't even try to pee!
My dog Arthur isn't scared of anything!
Not a mouse, not an acorn, not even a baboon!
But one thing he's afraid of is a balloon!

Archie Ridley (8)
The Grey House School

Gone To Sleep With The Angels

My grandad went to sleep with the angels
On the 29th of June this year you know,
I want to show all how I loved him so.

His rosy cheeks and Irish voice and chatter,
His greyish hair, his checked flat cap,
He loved to sing songs from his Dublin City,
A glass of Guinness or a drop of whisky every day -
Grandad told me it would keep the germs away!

He loved to tell me tales of old just like it was yesterday -
A red London bus for his Christmas present, with some
Nuts and an apple in a pillow case was all he received.
He remembered this to me every year when
I was surrounded by a carpet of presents.
But even so he was still full of good old Christmas cheer
And how I will miss him this year.

He would tell me when at school just to try my best,
And was so pleased when I got 16 out of 16 in my spelling test,
Grandad said I will do well,
If my days at school are my happiest ones.

At bedtime grandad would always say,
'Night-night, God bless, see you in the morning, please God'
And when the morning came,
He, as usual, was delighted to see me again.
'Good morning, Declan and how are you?
Irish sausages and eggs in the pan just for us two.'

He loved me from the very moment I was born
And the day he left us all, my heart was torn.
A joke, a song, a cup of tea,
Something always brings my grandad
Michael Smith back to me.

Declan Wagstaff (9)
The Grey House School

Ye Olde Duel

'Thy sword doth weave, little one,'
The drunken man did taunt,
His adversary ducked up and down,
Like the raising of the sun.

The little one was wearied
His foe was at his last,
His fearsome strong blows
Were like the river flows
All heavy on the wood.

The little one
He heard a creak
And gave a mighty leap
Out through the door,
Across the floor, as the timber beams did fall.

And never again,
Was the drunkard seen
Anywhere on the map.

Guy Bishop (10)
The Grey House School

My Cousin

My cousin has spiky hair like a
Hedgehog's back with really, really sharp spikes
And he has twenty pairs of shoes
And has ten shelves full up with Xbox games.
He has a bunk bed and he always
Goes on holiday with me.
His name's Christopher and he is sixteen
And is very annoying.

Matthew Bruce (7)
The Grey House School

The Lion's Tale

It's swift and fast and scary,
It uses its claws to capture prey,
Its voice is deep and fearful
As it hunts late in the day.

He crouches down to the earth below
And waits not daring to make a sound,
Then when he sees something bound towards him
He'll pounce and bring it down.

Then after dinner it stumbles back
To its lair deep in the caves
And it'll curl up tight and close its eyes
And sleep until the day.

Have you guessed what it is yet?
I'll tell you now . . . it's a lion
The king of the caves.

Beckie Bundy (11)
The Grey House School

Murphy

My grandma had a dog,
His name was Murphy,
I used to take him on his walks with my grandpa,
Up the road and through the Glen,
We go to look at the animals in the Glen,
But
Now that's all changed
Because old Murphy's dead.
Murphy was a big black dog with big floppy ears
But
When I was seven, Murphy was blind and could only see a bit.

Matthew Bell (8)
The Grey House School

Seasons Of The Year

S easons of the year are spring, summer, autumn and winter,
E very season is full of fun,
A ll the flowers in spring,
S ummer's fun to go and swim in the swimming pool,
O n autumn days with all its leaves,
N ever forget winter with all its snow,
S o have lots of fun all year through.

O range, brown and yellow in autumn,
F reezing cold in winter.

T he different colours in spring,
H olidays in summer,
E very season is great.

Y ou can have a play in every season,
E ven on the cold days,
A nd on the hot days,
R emember any season is *fun!*

Louise Hill (11)
The Grey House School

Jasper

I have a funny little cat,
His name is Jasper,
I think he is funny because
He winks at people,
He even sometimes jumps back on his hind legs,
And catches bubbles.
And when I come to feed him
He always comes near his dish
At night I like to cuddle him and
He makes me feel happy.

Sacha Patston (7)
The Grey House School

The Eagle

The eagle's eyes are
full of burning fire
and pure evil.
He comes and he goes
as he likes, he rules
the world of birds.
There is nothing he fears
except humans.
He comes from a
world of evil from
the depths of Hell.
He was born a killer
and will die a killer.
He rips and tears out
the animal's heart -
and feasts like
there's no tomorrow.

Daniel Curry (11)
The Grey House School

My Dad

My dad is very funny,
He likes to play jokes on me
But
I don't find them funny.
I don't know why he giggles with glee.
He scares me by hiding under the sofa and
Jumping up suddenly,
You don't know what he is going to do
So
Beware!

Anand Sankar (7)
The Grey House School

The Night He Died

I was there, with him
He was begging me to go
He told me he will die if I don't go
So I went but it was horrible
It happened again and again and again
On the 31st October he said goodbye
He had a gun pointing to his head
Bang! Blood went everywhere
Some was on my shoe
The police were there
They accused me of doing it
But my fingerprints were on it
I don't know how
But that is why I'm writing this poem
I'm in the . . . prison.

Charles Waite-Roberts (11)
The Grey House School

My Snoring Daddy

My daddy snores all through the night,
He is like a snoring, roaring bear,
That always wakes me up.
Every morning I am always droopy and
I need sleep.
One morning I was so tired, my head fell into the bowl!
Oh, my daddy is a snoring man and he is always annoying,
I am really sleepy all the time.

William Barnes (7)
The Grey House School

The Butterfly And The Animals

The butterfly goes here and there,
As he flies round a juicy pear,
Apples, bananas, lemons or limes,
He doesn't care, he eats them all the time.

The monkey, he's cheeky with glee,
As he swings among the winding trees,
Playing with his monkey friend,
As if the day would never end.

The elephant with his trunk so long,
And it's obvious that he's strong
Marching in his great big herd,
From a distance they're like a flock of birds.

Alex Holman (11)
The Grey House School

Polar Bear

Lumbering along on the thick ice,
Searching for his prey,
The cool, sharp wind,
Silently making its way through the thick white fur.

Disguised from his prey,
Looking like a big block of ice,
Quickly he plunges his thick, white paw,
Down a hole in the ice.

A quick but painful death,
For the poor animal,
That happens to be passing by,
It really is the survival of the fittest.

Alice Krasno (11)
The Grey House School

Cravings

Around and around her head turned
As the drops of cannabis got to work,
As her mind was poisoned with thoughts of drugs,
She took it again and again.

Her blood was black with pain and anger,
And she pictured the veins all pierced and swollen,
As her body thrived and craved for more,
Her purse was empty and she begged for more.
As each drop soothed her soul,
She lingered on with nothing more,
Than the taste for drugs, till she lay on the floor!

Lydia Amatt (11)
The Grey House School

My Cat

My cat is a sly cat,
His eyes can be full of hate,
Never get on his bad side,
Or he will use you as bait.

My cat creeps out of the door,
To catch a flock of birds,
He goes to the fields,
And sees cows in a herd.

He goes across the road,
To the other street,
Then he comes right back
And curls beside my feet.

Megan Dellaway (10)
The Grey House School

The Dragon

The dragon, it lives in the sewer
Deep underground
With lots of other mythical creatures
The Centaur, the Miniator and the Cyclops.

The dragon has eight legs
Each with five claws on them,
Giant wings the size of an albatross,
And a body the size of a mammoth.

The dragon is a special dragon
It can swim underwater
And fire massive fireballs
And soar all the way to Heaven.

The dragon's lair is filled with gold and silver
Rubies and sapphires, emeralds and diamonds,
His wings have more power than the fastest plane
And his claws could destroy solid metal.

The dragon can fly faster than the speed of light
And is as clever as fifty humans,
His tail could easily knock down a house
And is the size of ten elephants.

The dragon lives
And he shall live for a thousand more years,
Until he falls down from the sky,
And then he shall die a painful death.

Adam Perryman (11)
The Grey House School

The Thing

It rustled in the bushes,
It slowly crept out,
It padded across the garden
And through the flowerbeds,
A frog suddenly
Hopped into view,
But it never saw the light again,
And as I watched,
Out came one badger cub,
Then another,
Which squealed as it came into view,
Then as suddenly as they had come . . .
They were gone!

Emma Yeoman (11)
The Grey House School

Autumn

Deep crimson leaves shining in a ball
Light, glossy brown chestnuts ready to fall
The quacking and howling of the geese as they go by
The gentle breeze of air as they fly.

The whistling of the wind as it blows off the leaves
That the early autumn wind has whisked off the trees
The crackling and crunching as leaves are stamped on
As memories of summer are forgotten when the sun had shone.

Annie Appleton (10)
The Grey House School

Not Good For Everyone!

It's not good for everyone,
Dogs, cats, rabbits, wild animals!
They're scared of them so . . .
Keep your pets inside
Don't bring them out,
The illuminating fireworks may scare your little pets!
The whirling Catherine wheels burning showers of rockets!
The blazing bonfire of smoke scorching people's faces,
The poor little animals but . . .
Some don't mind the fireworks,
Bonfires, Roman candles and flashes of sparkles,
But keep your dogs, cats, rabbits,
Any animals inside for Bonfire Night.

Louise Ingham (9)
The Grey House School

The Lion's March

The lion creeping up on its prey,
Which is completely unaware that one of the most vicious
Beasts is about to strike,
As the lion draws closer his prey senses something is wrong
And alerts the rest of the herd,
Suddenly the lion sprints towards the herd,
He singles out one that looks weak,
As the rest of the herd scrample,
The lion leaps and brings the wildebeest to the ground.

Ben Read (10)
The Grey House School

Cameron's Alphabet

A is for alligator, watch where you swim.
B is for blood, all over your body.
C is for Cameron, that's little young me.
D is for Dad, he cares for me.
E is for exterminate all soppy toys.
F is for food fight with the kids from next door.
G is for Godzilla, that big beast.
H is for hippo, the pet that I wanted.
I is for Ivy that little young girl.
J is for jamjar where I keep this bee.
K is for killer, the cat from next door.
L is for lion that gave a loud roar.
M is for monsters who think they are scary.
N is for naughty, that's a description of me.
O is for octopus, great fun to wrestle.
P is for pirates attacking a vessel.
Q is for Quasimodo, the guy with the hump.
R is for Rottweiler, I made one jump.
S is for snake that bit my mum.
T is for terror, that's what they call me.
U is for underpants which I filled with curry.
V is for vampire who left in a hurry.
W is for werewolf really hairy.
X is for X-rated my midnight feast.
Y is for yo yo, my tricks are so great.
Z is for zombie, my very best mate.
    So I'll ABC you later.

Cameron Gaul (8)
The Grey House School

In The Graveyard

I'm walking through the graveyard
On a cold and misty night
Looking out for vampires and werewolves
That may be in sight
For Satan is the Dark Lord of Hell
For his evil potions will get his revenge.
So I'm walking through the gravestones.
With the flowers that were once beautiful.
But Satan has destroyed them, I turned around
There's a vampire in sight with its blood dripping phlegm.
I ran back to my house
Where doom cannot spread
But just so you know I'm already dead.

Katharine Whittingham (8)
The Grey House School

The Months

January is very cold, icicles and snow
February is a dull month, it's just cold
March is when all of the daffodils come out
April is when birds sing, flowers spring
May is pretty, look at all the flowers
June is a hot month so get in the pool
July is the hottest month so go to the beach
August is lovely and sunny, but sometimes scatters of showers
September is when apples grow on the apple tree
October is when the leaves change colour
November is when the trees are bare, tall and grey
December is exciting, Christmas is nearly here
And they're the months of the year.

Tara Kirby (8)
The Grey House School

The Seasons

Spring is quite hot - quite cold.
Very beautiful with snowdrops and daffodils
Other flowers too, with sunshine and frost.
Icicles, the dew on the lawn,
It sparkles like the stars.
Summer is very hot, great fun.
Daisies, tulips, pansies and buttercups all open.
We can run around but beware of the wasps.
We can sunbathe and eat lunch and tea outside
But the best part is going in the paddling pool,
And having water fights.
Autumn is cold, bare trees,
Piles of leaves.
It's misty and frosty
And we have to rake up the leaves,
Well, it's quite fun - but not quite
Winter is very, very cold with snow and icy roads.
Now it's Christmas
But now it's spring again for you.

Alexandra Moore (9)
The Grey House School

Skateboarding

To skateboard,
First you need to get a skateboard
And some pads,
A helmet,
Two elbow pads,
One, two knee pads
And some gloves.
Then you need a place to skateboard!
Find a hill or somewhere flat,
Then you're ready to go like that!

Alexander Bruce (9)
The Grey House School

The Alphabet

A is for Albert, picking his nose
B is for Beth, eating her toes
C is for Charlie eating crisps
D is for Darren swimming around
E is for Eleanor eating eggs
F is for Fergus sitting down
G is for George thinking all the time
H is for Harry laughing all the time
I is for India exploring everywhere
J is for Jordan moving everywhere
K is for Keith eating cardboard
L is for Lucy twirling around
M is for Mike eating Mars bars
N is for Nick hammering nails
O is for Oscar eating oranges
P is for Percy eating purses
Q is for Quentin eating quickly
R is for Richard doing nothing
S is for Stephen walking along
T is for Tom fighting with a sock
U is for Ursula sleeping all the time
V is for Victor vanishing all the time
W is for William waffling all the time
X is for X-Men eating maps
Y is for Yvonne eating yo-yos
Z is for Zelda fitting on a zebra.

Fergus Corcoran (8)
The Grey House School

Dennis's Alphabet

A is for alligator, that nasty old beast
B is for blood all in your body
C is for Calum that's little young me
D is for Dad he's kind to me
E is for exterminate all soppy toys
F is food fight with those Bash Street Boys
G is for Godzilla, the massive great beast
H is for hippo, the pet that I wanted
I is for Ivy the little young girl
J is for jamjar where I keep the bee
K is for killer, next door's cat
L is for lion who gave a loud roar
M is for monsters who think they are scary
N is for naughty, a description of me
O is for octopus, great fun to wrestle
P is for pirates attacking a vessel
Q is for Quasimodo the guy with the hump
R is for Rottweiler, I made one jump
S is for serpent who bit my mum
T is for terror what they call me
U is for underpants filled with curry
V is for vampire left in a hurry
W is for werewolf very hairy
X is for X-rated my midnight feast
Y is for yo-yo, my tricks are great
Z is for zombie, my very best mate.

So I'll ABC you later.

Calum Windeatt (8)
The Grey House School

World War I Death Sentence

With the trenches below,
And the bombers above,
With the gunfire deafening,
And the generals shouting,
My gravestone awaits,
My death sentence is near.

The shells exploding,
The bullet marks deep,
The rats always near,
This is Hell's deep.

Plane carcasses falling,
The anti-aircraft guns blaring,
My gravestone shaking,
My heart pumping.

My shiny boots now muddy and dirty,
The hat I'm wearing now creased and torn.
My hair full of lice,
And something tells me
My death sentence is . . .
Near.

Alex Bond (10)
The Grey House School

Snowfall

Snow fell all around
Covering all of the ground,
Icicles hang on window ledge
Children playing with a sledge.

Turkeys done,
Come on everyone,
Gather round and eat.

Sarah Henshaw (10)
The Grey House School

The White Stuff

Snow glorious snow
Cold, hard, white and beautiful
These are the ingredients of a thing called snow
Whipped cream all around you
As sweet as pineapple
A layer of white sheet all around the world
Ice on a pond as thick as a ruler
I wake, look outside, our lawn as white as paper
I rush outside, so beautiful,
I don't even dare to step on it.
Oooh! there goes my dog Stanley
Stomping all over it.
Oh well, there's always tomorrow.

Gabriel Cattermull (10)
The Grey House School

The Witches Chant

Sizzle, sizzle, fizzle, fizzle,
We are trying to make you grizzle.
Put in a bird, put in a frog,
Put in a lizard and even a dog.
Big bears' claws
And little cats paws,
Golden lion's mane,
But just a bit of rain.
Big hawk's wing,
Buzzing bee's sting,
A little girl's hair,
Now all children *beware!*

Becky Wilson (9)
The Grey House School

Annoying Brother

Today my brother was such a pain,
He kept on tapping on my shoulder,
Asking the same questions again and again.
But later something different he said,
It really annoyed me,
So I punched him in the head.
He thought, *that's not fair,*
So he crept up behind me and shouted,
'How do you want to start it!'
'Start what?' I said.

Then I found myself lying in a hospital bed,
With a very big bump upon my head.
I got out of my bed and started a fight,
But then I found out I was dreaming
Through the night.

Christopher Gilks (10)
The Grey House School

Snow

Snow is sparkly
Snow is bright
Snow is pretty
Snow is white
Snow is cold
Snow is crispy
But melts away
Overnight.

Samantha Fuhrmann (9)
The Grey House School

The Sunset That Brought Me To Life

We went to the hillside on that day
And there we saw a bundle of hay
And there we sat all that day
Thinking and talking about me.

I then said to you, 'Why am I thee?'
Then I gave a little wee yawn
And then I noticed it was dawn
I said to you, 'Why am I here?'
Then I noticed it was all clear,
That God had brought me here.

Then I looked up into the sky
And I saw not a fly,
But the most beautiful thing,
It was the shape of half a ring.
It was bright,
As bright can be,
But I did not know thee.

Then I felt an amazing thing,
And I thought it must be the ring.
Then I felt an explosion of life
And I thought it must be my life
That this wonderful ring has brought me,
And now I am . . . me.

Elle Todd (9)
The Grey House School

Snow

Snow is like a thick, white carpet
All around the world.
I want the snow to last forever.
So we can have snowball fights every day
And our snowman will not melt.
I know the snow has to go
Because the snow has many places to go to.

Lily Stevens (10)
The Grey House School

The Little Old Lady

I'm the little old lady,
the lady who lives under a cow,
the lady who prays to God.
I'm the little old lady,
the lady who has no hair,
the lady who has a bird for her leg.
I'm the little old lady,
the lady who begs for money,
the lady who plays with boys and girls.
I'm the little old lady
who's thanking you for reading this poem.

Mariella Hancock (9)
The Grey House School

The Cat

Fluffy ears and cotton tail
Sleeps cuddled up and tight
Steps silent in the night
Claws sharp like knives
But the cat does have nine lives
A snout like a bear
The cat does not scare
The cat walks alone until the end doth come.

Matthew Brown (9)
The Grey House School

Snow

Snow looks like cream
Or a white chocolate beam,
You might have a dream
Of some tasty ice cream.

You might spot snowmen hidden behind hedges
Or children happily playing on sledges,
You'll see footprints on the ground
And children playing without a sound,
Playing in the bright, white light.

Ben Perryman (9)
The Grey House School

Winter Snow

The crunch of the snow
The sparkle of the frost
The coldness of the air
A blowing breeze
Freezing cold
The wet grass covered with snow
Sparkles with glamour.
They are the things I love about *snow!*

Emily Fearon (10)
The Grey House School

Looking At A School

It was an ordinary school
yellow and grey.
I got shown round by
a student.
Mum and Dad got shown
round by a teacher.

The girl wasn't very nice.
She looked at me
in a horrible way.
I went outside to play
with the other boys and girls.

Then I went back inside
to be shown round some more.
I went to the pool.

It was quite small.
The girl called Jane
thought I was a pain
and pushed me into the pool.

My clothes were ruined.
I swam to the side
and got out.
By then Jane had disappeared.
Mum and Dad
came in with the teacher.

'What happened?' said Mum.
I told them all about it.
Jane got really badly told off
and I found a better school!

Alexia Hall (10)
The Grey House School

Winter Is . . .

Winter is snowflakes floating down.
Iced up windowpanes.
Caught by the fire.
Glistening, sparky, sparkly, glittering spiderwebs.
Cats stretched out by the fire.
Snow angels glitter in the moonlight.
Freezing ice.
Birds fly south for winter.
Shimmering snow.
Crackling snow spread all around.
Warm boots, warm hats, warm scarves and warm gloves.
Children out in snow.
Snowmen talking, snowballs thrown.
Wrapped in snow.

Georgina Leeming (8)
Whitewater CE Primary School

Why Christmas Is Special To Me

C is for Christ, the birth of Jesus,
H is for happiness to share,
R is for real happiness in love,
 I is for incredible, the star that is shining,
S is for shepherds, who saw Jesus,
T is for tree, a Christmas tree,
M is for magic, the joy that it brings,
A is for amazing in Christmas' love,
S is for Santa a magical man.

Caitlin O'Sullivan (8)
Whitewater CE Primary School

My Winter Walk

There are bare skeletons reaching up to the cold blue sky
Icy teeth hanging from the branches
Crispy leaves, crunching when I walk
No berries except the holly
Hungry, thirsty birds
Search for food and water
Hopping over the snowy ground
A dog leaving a track of prints on a field's blanket

Horses huddled together in the stable
Away from the cold weather
I am alone because no one is out
Everyone is indoors
Snuggled in their beds
It's time to go home and sit by the fire.

Gemma Hitchcock (9)
Whitewater CE Primary School

Winter Is . . .

Winter is so sparkly and cold,
So lovely are the icicles.
The lovely snow is so glittery and sparkly.
Now it's the wonderful season full of lots of different things.
Cats by the fire so cosy and warm.
Snow so soft and fluffy.
Carol songs fill the air.
This is the sign of winter.

Emily Belcher (7)
Whitewater CE Primary School

Autumn

A utumn is fun
U nder my feet there are leaves
T he leaves make great leaf prints
U nder a mountain of shavings are hedgehogs
M ummy lets us feed the animals
N uts are collected by the squirrels

I have bought a bird table for food and shelter
S un makes a lovely sunset

R eally magic colour on the leaves
E arly in the morning I see a bold brown stag
A h, lovely wildlife awakes me
L ate in the mornings
L onger nights, shorter days
Y ellow, orange, russet carpet

F oxes make a snuggly bed of crunching leaves
U nder the kennel is my sleeping dog
N obody wants to go outside because it's so cold.

Florence Perry (9)
Whitewater CE Primary School

Winter Is . . .

Frozen icicles,
Lakes like ice,
Crunching snow when you tread on it,
Sparkling cobwebs,
Snow so fluffy.
Snowflakes falling to the ground and melting,
Snowballs ready to be thrown,
Snowmen are ready to be made,
Sitting by the cosy fire,
Hot water bottles in our beds to keep us warm,
Because here comes the snow,
The wonderful snow.

Nerys Nabbs (7)
Whitewater CE Primary School

Autumn Angels

They are lifted,
Like angels off the trees.
Lifted by their master,
The wind.
The angels of the trees
Whisper to me
Like a friend with a secret
They are desperate to tell.
Suddenly, a fiery blaze
Lights up, full of leaves
Of all different shades,
Shapes and sizes.
Conkers, acorns, helicopters
Whizz and fly in a big whirlwind.
Tightening and loosening
Throughout the day.
Crispy leaves
Like angels fluttering down
Before me from the sky.
Gently, softly,
Swooping down
Like a feather or a bird.

Elizabeth Floyd (9)
Whitewater CE Primary School

Winter Is . . .

Sparkling spiderwebs like diamonds.
Cats by the fire, stretching for sleep.
Clean, silent night for the cats to rest.
Footsteps in the snow.
Snow angels singing.
Trees dropping snow.

Daniel Brooks (8)
Whitewater CE Primary School

Winter Is . . .

Cats by the fire,
White, fluffy snow,
Spiderwebs sparkle like diamonds,
Snowflakes floating down,
Icy rivers,
Ice on windowpanes,
Building snowmen,
I love winter!

Sam Hewlett (8)
Whitewater CE Primary School

Winter Is . . .

Cold and frosty
The spiderwebs sparkle
Footsteps in the snow
Icicles glisten sharply.

Oliver Bushnell (7)
Whitewater CE Primary School

Winter Is . . .

Winter is shiny and sparkly,
Snow falling from the sky,
Frosty leaves crackling
As you stand on them,
Warm scarf for a cold winter,
Curling up by the fire,
I like winter!

Benjamin White (7)
Whitewater CE Primary School

My Autumn Poem

As I wander through fields
I view golden brown trees as I pass by.
Winds blow the leaves in a swirling,
Whooshing and whirling ring.
Trees all golden brown,
Leaves fall from above you like a shower of fiery leaves.

As I wander some more
The leaves rustle beneath my feet,
While they drift down from above.
Trees all empty,
Trees all clean.

When I go to school
I look at the slides
With leaves sliding down the slope,
Leaving a trail of crystal beads.

Days get shorter,
Days get colder and winds get faster.

Max Davies (9)
Whitewater CE Primary School

Winter Is . . .

Cats by the fire snuggled up.
Snow - glittery, shiny and sparkly.
Frosty icicles hanging from the trees.
People making footprints, happy and laughing.
Keeping warm, making snowballs.

Megan Head (7)
Whitewater CE Primary School

Winter Is . . .

Icy water freezing,
Icy, fluffy snow
Snowflakes falling to the ground clean,
Silent and frosty,
Snowflakes sparkle like diamonds.
Silver spider webs, sparkle very sharply,
Diamonds cold.
Building snowmen.
Having snow fights.
Foxes in their dens.
The snow as fluffy as cotton wool.
Hills glitter.
Frosty branches.
As cold as icicles.

Josh Capon (8)
Whitewater CE Primary School

Winter Is . . .

Snow
Ice
Frosty icicles
Snowy windows
Slushy roads
Sparkling spiders' webs
People in igloos
Cat on the fire
Snowflakes sparkle
I'm sending Santa's letter.

Jonathan Sharp (8)
Whitewater CE Primary School

Winter Poem

As I walk in the winter
Snow falls down on top of the trees
Floating, twisting, turning like soft cotton wool
In the cities snow falling down on top of people
The grey, blue sky full of snowflakes and frost
Kids make snowmen in their gardens
They have snowball fights
And snowmen stand still like frozen statues

Ponds get really icy and the ice is hard like glass
The sun shines on the glass and it glistens
I see snow on top of the branches like icing on a cake
Birds calling for food in their nests
These are the things I see in the winter.

Connor Gains (8)
Whitewater CE Primary School

Autumn Days

Golden yellow,
Ruby red,
Golden brown leaves,
Falling from the cool grey sky

Busy hedgehogs,
Cold hedgehogs,
Burrowing through chestnuts,
Acorns and conkers.

Wind whistles by,
As the leaves dance in the sky.

Jade Evans (8)
Whitewater CE Primary School

Winter Is . . .

Snow falling onto the ground.
Water frozen solid.
Bright icicles.
Sharp icicles.
Trees not moving.
Frozen windows.
Lots of snowmen and snowballs.

Sam Grotier
Whitewater CE Primary School

Winter Is . . .

As cold as icicles.
The snow is as fluffy as cotton wool.
Sparkly, silvery and shiny.
Silent as mice.
Frosty benches.
Building snowmen.
Having snow fights.
Foxes hiding in their dens.

Samuel Drew (7)
Whitewater CE Primary School

Winter Is . . .

Winter is glittery and there is clean snow,
Freezing in the wind,
Spider webs sparkle like diamonds,
Snowflakes float to the ground,
Frosty, cold, icy snow,
Cats by the fire.

Victoria Baker (8)
Whitewater CE Primary School

Gold, Brown, Red And Yellow

Gold is the beautiful colour that sometimes the leaves will turn.
Gold is the colour of rough, bumpy bark.
Gold is that warm fire that you rush inside to see.
Gold is the wild dormouse ready for hibernation.
Gold is an autumn colour.

Brown is the many leaves on trees and on the ground.
Brown is the muddy puddle I jump in.
Brown is my wet and muddy jumper.
Brown is the last of the birds flying south.
Brown is an autumn colour.

Red is the bright fiery leaves falling like fairies.
Red is the robin's breast that's so colourful.
Red is the colour you see every morning
                    telling you it's going to be a rainy day.
Red is the last apple coming from the tree.
Red is an autumn colour.

Yellow is the gleaming sun that shines every morning.
Yellow is the dancing leaves that fall tree by tree.
Yellow is the last daffodil still hanging on.
Yellow is the caterpillar crawling across the leaf.
Yellow is an autumn colour.

Beth Luckett (9)
Whitewater CE Primary School

What Christmas Means To Me

C hristmas tree
H appy families
R eally special
I cy tree
S tar on the top of the tree
T he best time in the year
M ince pies and custard
A ngels
S nuggle by the fire.

Robert Miller (7)
Whitewater CE Primary School

Autumn

The leaves change to colours brown and gold,
They scatter along the ground.
They dance and twirl in the wind,
Like actors on a stage.

Wearing costumes of gold, amber and tan.
Rustling, crackling and crunching,
As they say their words.
Cool, cold evenings.
Some animals hibernate,
Swallows fly south to warmer climates.
I shall see them again in spring.

George Miller (9)
Whitewater CE Primary School

Autumn Fairy

She sweeps down,
Zapping the leaves with her wand.
They turn to gold, bronze, chestnut, scarlet.
She plucks the leaves off the trees,
Until they are bare.
The leaves glide down
And crash into frost-covered ground.

She shoos the birds away,
She kicks the sun
So it loses its power.
She sprinkles frost to the hard ground.

Is there no stopping the autumn fairy?

Jack Mitchell (9)
Whitewater CE Primary School

Autumn Poem

I can hear leaves falling down,
I can hear them crackling,
Red, orange, brown, green, yellow.
The colours spin round my head,
Tumbling down from tree to tree
As they spin a whirling pattern.

As I skip through layers of leaves
I follow the maze to find the colour
Of all the golden leaves rustling,
Crackling, crunching goes the leaves
As they try to escape from the tree.
It is windy, cold and frosty
The night is still,
Full of moonlight the cold winds
Whistle in the breeze,
They make autumn really cold,
Some of the animals hibernate.
It seems so quiet
As we hear these leaves fall down.

Siân Nabbs (9)
Whitewater CE Primary School

Winter Is . . .

Fluffy snow glistening in the night sky
As icicles float down.
Clean snow all around us,
Frosty, freezing ice.

Heather Marnoch (7)
Whitewater CE Primary School

I Am Winter

I am winter
I make the world stand still
By covering everything
With my soft woolly blanket of snow.

I am winter
I turn the trees into icy fingers
By touching them with my frozen fingers.
Making them shiver.

I am winter
I paint your windows with my glittery nails
Then I cover it with snow
Making it like a maze. .

Nancy Scally (8)
Whitewater CE Primary School

Winter Days

Snowy frost
Drifting down
Onto icy fields all around
Frosty winds
Whizzing through my hair
Icy patterns silver and clear
Winter going
Spring to come
Rabbits hibernating under the ground
Bare trees blowing in the bitter wind
Hearing robins sing at dawn
Icy puddles and freezing ponds
Children playing and shouting, 'Yippy!'
'Wow!'
'This is fun!'

Siân Brooks (9)
Whitewater CE Primary School

Jack Frost The Winter Fairy

As I spread my wings so wide
Swooping gently as I glide

As I sprinkle frost around
Dancing, swirling to the ground

As I touch every tree
So frosty white this village will be

Just before the break of dawn
I whiten everybody's lawn

As the end of the night
I make sure everything's white

Now it's dawn and I have to go
So children can play in the glistening snow.

Dominique Cooper (8)
Whitewater CE Primary School

Autumn Wonders

Cloudy skies mist around,
Sycamore seeds whirling to the ground,
Crops are waving in their lawn,
It's maize, it's wheat and also corn.
Frosty chill in the air,
All the trees are turning bare.
Fiery colours skidding along,
Every bird is singing its song.
While I'm trudging through the fiery sea,
Autumn leaves are following me.
The colours are like burning brown,
While they are twirling down.

Jack Corley (8)
Whitewater CE Primary School

Night

His face is like a hollow shell,
With burning coals as eyes.
His mouth is a line
That never opens.

His clothes, a black cloak,
With a red lace of fire.
A hood hides his face,
But you don't want to see it.

He rides on the back of nightmares,
Stealthily, all through the night.
Gliding along like a bird,
Always on the move, never tiring.

Helena Clough (9)
Whitewater CE Primary School

Night

As the sun goes in, night comes out.
He wears a big cloak,
Which covers the sky,
Like a bird fluttering by.
He makes no sound,
While travelling around.
The moon shines bright,
Leading the way.
As children sleep,
Night comes by,
Sprinkling stars around the sky.
As the sun comes out,
He gathers his cloak.
And off, like the wind,
He goes away,
To come back later that day.

Rebecca Mark (10)
Whitewater CE Primary School

The Curse Of Night

Ye night hath conquered space, moons
And half of Earth the small.
To stop ye taking more and more
We've called an anti-black ball.

The sun will rebel against ye powers,
Protecting Earth the small.
By the time simmering sun is done,
Ye won't be there at all!
By the Gods, what it is like living
With the curse and stupid sun.

My red slit eyes watch and try,
To scare that stupid sun.
However hard I try I find,
The damage I do is none.

Stupid sun sits there, placidly,
Watching my warrior stars.
The planets go round sun smiling,
Half light and half dark.

I'll get revenge some time,
When sun is old and poor.
Then space will become eternally black,
And I will become the core.

Kerry Corley (10)
Whitewater CE Primary School

Snow

S eeing my cousins.
N o fighting.
O n a sleigh.
W indows glowing.

Charlie Stephen (7)
Whitewater CE Primary School

Winter Bird

As I sail through the sky
I see the frosty world below
With the winter sun setting low in the sky

The snowflakes fall swiftly down
Like feathers gliding from the sky
I dive down to the river and find it solid, hard like a mirror of ice

I fly softly back to the nest
The swirly snowflakes block my path
I find an abandoned nest cradled in the dark fingers of a tree
I shuffle my feathers and shiver.

Georgie White (9)
Whitewater CE Primary School

Autumn

As I walk through the forest
I see amber, red, tan, orange and golden brown leaves.
I hear rustling, crunching, crackling
And crispy leaves from every step I make.

I see leaves swirling up from the ground like a whirlwind.
I hear birds tweeting, chattering and singing.

I see trees swaying with the colours blending in together.
I hear the wind whispering to the trees.

William Murray (9)
Whitewater CE Primary School

The First Adventure of Twlobby

Twlobby is an elf of Boggartsh Forest City,
He has amazing adventures outside the city.
He's about to fight the Nunquams of Flybolob Woods,
Strange, funny creatures with quagling hoods.

He packed his bag and grabbed his sword,
His father said, 'Be careful of the oozing fords.'
'Father, Father don't worry about me,
I'll kill them Nunquams and make history.'

He quietly crept into Flybolob Woods,
Looking for the Nunquams with quagling hoods.
He found them frogging in the ford,
But they were ready, they had their swords.

The fight began between Twlobby the small,
Against the Nunquams big and tall,
Twlobby grasped his languishing sword,
He plunged it into their hearts and put the bodies in the ford.

Twlobby ran back to the city carrying a quagling hood,
He shouted, 'Father I have come back from Flybolob Woods!'
His father replied, 'How would I know?'
'I stole a hood from our evil foe!'

Twlobby has a wall inside his room,
It's next to a cupboard for all his brooms.
On there he keeps the things from his adventures,
Like a quagling hood from his first adventure.

Edward Blunden (10)
Whitewater CE Primary School

Night

Night is ever travelling,
Travelling like the wind.
His starlight eyes dazzling,
Followed by the twoot and flutter of owl wings.

He has no feet and floats around,
Never tripping.
Leaving no trace or sound,
As nearby a stream is dripping.

His face is lavender grey,
But his hands are hidden.
Here comes day,
He must leave,
Leave in the shadows.

Richard Nutton (11)
Whitewater CE Primary School

Winter Poem

Snow falls down like a huge white blanket
Bitter winds from all around
Trees stand like black skeletons
Glistening sharp icicles dropping down
Swirling snowflakes drift down like confetti.

Hannah Cutler (8)
Whitewater CE Primary School